CORPORATE
SAFARI

Raj Pillai

Wisdom Village Publications Pvt. Ltd.
Knowledge is information. Wisdom is transformation

A WISDOM VILLAGE PRESENTATION

Books from Wisdom Village Publications envision to enhance and enrich their readers with life changing experiences from the business, mind, body and soul genres. They strive towards holistic development.

Editorial Coordinator : Anu Anand

This novel is entirely a work of fiction. The names, characters and incidents portrayed in it are the work of the author's imagination and not to be construed as real. Any resemblance to actual persons, living or dead, events or localities, is entirely coincidental.

ISBN 9789380710266

Published in 2013 by:

 Wisdom Village Publications Pvt. Ltd.
Knowledge is information. Wisdom is transformation

WVPD is a part of Wisdom Village
649, O4U, Udyog Vihar, Phase V, Gurgaon, Haryana–122 001
www.wvpd.in

To Book Your Orders:
Email: wvpdindia@gmail.com
Or Call: +91 9810800469

Published by Anu Anand; *Cover Design* by Sunil Mathur; *Page Setting* by Mamta Sahni;

Printed by J.K. Offset Graphics (P) ltd, B-278, O.I.A, Phase-1, New Delhi-110 020.

DEDICATED
TO
MY FATHER

Justice N. Santosh Hegde
Former Judge, Supreme Court of India

Flat No. B-34, 2nd Floor
Embassay Palace Apartments,
No. 1/16, Cunningham Road,
Bangalore-560 052
Tel: No. 080-2234 3738

15th September, 2012

FOREWORD

I am pleased with the efforts taken by first time author Shri Raj Pillai for addressing a challenging subject very relevant to modern India and Indians, especially the youth. With falling moral values and dishonesty being the order of the day, it is very important to instill faith in young Indians that one need not to be unethical to be successful. One can be successful in his or in her life with right values provided the individual prepares himself or herself adequately to face the unscrupulous elements and adverse conditions they might be faced with. This very attribute is nicely illustrated by Mr. Raj Pillai in his book with a first-hand account of simple management tools which can be used by any professional fighting for his/her survival in modern corporate word.

I wish Mr. Raj Pillai all the very best in his venture.

(N. Santosh Hegde)

CONTENTS

CONTENTS

INTRODUCTION

We Indians are going through a huge transition. This change is evident in every walk of life. To name a few, the way communication was carried out in the 80's and 90's is way different from how it takes place today. The same applies to simple things like shopping. Today, even in smaller cities, we find malls filled with people from all sections of society unlike in the past where the local grocery shop dominated.

The change is no longer confined to big or tier 2 cities but has percolated down to smaller towns as well, like Chindwara, Manendragarh, Tumkur, Mavellikara or Bullandshahar. The electronic media has also played a vital role in bringing about this change, by reaching out to the public with information from across the world. With this, people's aspiration levels, especially of the youth, who incidentally form the country's majority, have gone up significantly. A very visible sign of this is that youngsters, whether from Sangli or Siliguri or Jodhpur, or Jabalpur, sport similar designer clothes and shoes (genuine or fake), depending upon their purchasing power. Similarly, if you visit a mall in any city, it would be inundated by youngsters. One of the reasons for this changed attitude is the economic reforms, which has brought capitalism into the forefront and ostentation is no longer considered a taboo.

However, the flipside is, today as a country we lack leaders with character who could be role models for the youth. More often than not people with dubious records and backgrounds are occupying positions of respect and power. This trend has also encouraged GREED in every sphere of activity. In fact, to be greedy is considered the same as being ambitious. Greed has also become the glue that is binding devious people together, helping them gain and sustain power, making it difficult for people with values and principles to preserve their dignity.

The most affected by this paradigm shift are the youth who subsequently think that one cannot do well in life by being honest and ethical. I have faced this situation at various colleges where I have been invited to share my experiences. The students there refuse to believe that it's possible to succeed with attributes like integrity and honesty, and I see this negativity in urban youth more than the youth with rural roots.

Greed has also become a key component in today's corporate world. In fact, it's more deep-rooted in the business world than anywhere else. Greed has also become the password for success in the business world and is causing havoc at micro and macro levels. It's driving innocent youngsters to chase mirages and pursue success at any cost because it's the end that matters, not the means — meaning all's fair and square as long as one wins! Today's corporate world is clearly divided between the ones who want success at any cost and the ones who listen to their conscience or retain their values. To quote the English poet, W.B Yeats, "We live in a world where the best lack all conviction, and the worst are full of passionate intensity." The sad part is that while the former are in abundance, the latter are a diminishing race.

Down the years, I have strongly believed in Pandit Nehru (first Prime Minister of independent India) who, in describing 'INDIANNESS' in his famous book 'Discovery of India' mentions how in spite of having to face several foreign invasions, India has always come out stronger, and one of the main reasons for this is our long-lasting, time-tested, sustainable middle-class value system. I am sure the current invasion in the form of greed would also tide over and we would evolve as a better and a stronger nation.

It is with this belief I have penned this book. It is based on the battle between the ethical TIGER, of strong character and the unscrupulous WILD DOGS of the corporate jungle. The wild dogs may win small battles but the tiger finally wins the big war and prevails. However, to do so, the tiger must continue to update his knowledge and skills. I sincerely hope that all bright sparks entering the corporate world, especially the ones from small towns who want to make it big in the corporate scenario, would read the book and sharpen their tigerly qualities.

———•———

1

WHY THE TIGER RULES THE JUNGLE

After three good days of a relaxed and rejuvenated holiday in Ooty, Raos were on their way back home to Bangalore. They were around Madumalai wild life sanctuary, when Meera, Raman Rao's wife, hesitatingly suggested that they make a stopover at one of the Madumalai forest guest houses. To her surprise and pleasure, the suggestion was cheerfully accepted by all, and soon there was a lively chatter among the group, wishing for the good time to continue some more. Kumar, whose family was also accompanying the Raos, immediately got into action and made a few phone calls to Chennai forest headquarters. Eventually, he secured them a place at the wild life sanctuary guest house.

The available accommodation, housed in an early 19th century building with charming architecture of exposed brick walls, comprised of two big dormitories, each with six cots. Raman, a big fan of such old buildings with high ceilings and skylights, was more than grateful to his wife Meera for her suggestion. And the best part was that, it was being looked after by a lady forest guard whose duties included preparing and serving hot food as well. The deal was very simple — she had to be provided with the ingredients for the day i.e. vegetables, chicken or meat and she'd then prepare food for a nominal charge of Rs 500 per day only! Within an hour of moving in they enjoyed tea and pakodas made by her, and couldn't be more pleased with their choice of accommodation. And with the fresh, unpolluted September breeze of the forest, the place was a real treat for an extended holiday. The whole thinking process felt enhanced and suddenly life started appearing even better.

The most excited member of the gang was Zoo-zoo, the Raos' pug dog. Straight off the car, he had plenty of space to run around and seemed quite bemused to see a huge stone sculptor of an elephant kept at the entrance of the building, a beast much larger than what his eyes would have ever scanned. Raman wished to sneak into Zoo-zoo's mind and understand his thoughts upon seeing something hundred times his size.

Before nightfall, Raman picked up the tickets for the early morning safari ride in the jungle scheduled for next day. Raman had been going on such safari rides at Bandipur, Nagerhole and Madumalai wild sanctuaries for the past fifteen years, yet had no clue what to expect the next day. Little did he realize how the next day's safari would reinforce his perception of the corporate world.

Raman's exposure to the forest had begun in the middle school, when he was put in a boarding school at Pachmarhi. Pachmarhi or Panchmarhi is located in the Satpura range of central India and derives its name from five natural caves, which are believed to have been the hide-out of the Pandavas during the days of Mahabharat. Today, Pachmarhi is known for more than three hundred waterfalls (there are so many of them that naming all must have become difficult, so they are simply called A, B, C and so on). It also has a few vantage points and hilltops like Sunset points, Dupgarh, Chowragarh and Pachmarhi hill, which are trekkers' delights. The entire belt is a biosphere reserve, with picturesque flora and fauna making walking and cycling sheer bliss. AEC (Army Education Corps) has occupied a vast area in the reserve and the army band fills the air with musical notes as the troops train.

Raman's days at Pachmarhi were the best days of his life. The call of the wild was so intense that one night, he dared to climb a hill close by along with his classmate. They were lucky not to be reprimanded by the warden or not to be lost!

MADUMALAI SAFARI

The first safari started at six in the morning. The Raos and Kumars were ushered into a twelve-seater Eicher vehicle accompanied by a forest guard. Once the vehicle started rolling, the guard explained the dos and don'ts of the trip. The safari ride, as told to them, usually took an hour. Over the years, Raman had developed an uncanny knack of guessing how the trip would turn out. This impromptu analysis would be based upon several signs and signals he would get at the time and such omens were coming through pretty strong that day. The vehicle moved around 2 kms on the Ooty-Mysore highway and then took one of the forest roads. The driver of the safari vehicle decided to choose that road in consultation with the guard and other forest employees. This selection decided the occupants' fate for the next hour! Raman had also learnt over the years that like the success probability of a movie, there was no guarantee of sighting wild animals in a forest.

As the vehicle slowly made way into the forest, the guard suddenly signaled to them to remain quite.

Complete silence descended the van. This was one of those moments when nerves were put to test, as every passing second was filled with expectation. Within minutes of the drive, the vehicle almost came to a halt next to a pack of foxes and a huge bison. The guard whispered that those weren't foxes but wild dogs, which in fact, had killed a baby bison and were now chasing the mother bison away. The mother bison was refusing to leave. He also mentioned that this was supposed to be one of the rarest sights in this setting, and he was witnessing it for the first time in his 25 years of service.

The next 30 minutes unfurled the most amazing scene. The wild dogs seemed in total sync in their attack. The entire pack of dogs was divided into sub-packs and these sub-packs were playing well-defined roles. One sub-pack was tearing the baby bison into pieces, the other one was busy chasing the mother bison away, the third sub-pack was keeping a close eye on the herd of bisons, who had abandoned the mother and baby bison. There was one more sub-pack which was giving cover to the whole operation. This group was also reinforcing the pack as and when required. On careful examination, you could see the distinctly long tail and longish jaw of these canines, unlike that of a common street dog.

When the vehicle finally moved away from this once-in-a-lifetime experience, there was absolute silence for the next ten minutes. The guard again asked the driver to slow down and announced in hush tone 'Tiger!' Raman thought that was the day of his life! Though the vehicle moved at snail's pace, no one could sight the big cat. After 10 to 15 minutes, when they were out of tiger territory which is usually a grassland, the guard said, "There was definitely a tiger around but the wild dogs' presence must have cautioned it."

After the three hour scenic drive from Madumalai to Mysore, Raman had no doubt about who ruled the forest. And he was sure that this applied to the CORPORATE JUNGLE too. The tiger denotes the guy who has the best attributes, plays by the rules and believes in going up the ladder based on his own merit, whereas, the wild dogs are a bunch of go-getters who are highly networked, closely knitted and support each other, ensuring that every big kill is shared between them, including the top positions. The wild dogs can go to any lengths to corner the tiger because the righteous tiger is self-respecting, will not stoop to any level to achieve his objective.

Incidentally wild dog packs are no longer confined to jungles, corporate or otherwise, but are everywhere now. They are a creation of reckless GREED in the capitalistic society that is evident in large scale scams and rampant corruption which keeps popping its hydra head frequently.

———•———

2

THE CUB'S GROWING YEARS

Raman was one of those privileged sons whose father loved him absolutely and unconditionally. His father never lost his cool with him for any of his mistakes and continued to love him more throughout his growing up years. Raman's every demand was met with an 'ask one, get two' approach. He also encouraged Raman to be a good human being with his exemplary life. Raman had never come across a single soul who had any differences with his father, or for that matter, to whom his father ever talked ill about.

Another of his father's strong influences on him was his religious inclination. Raman's childhood was spent in Madhya Pradesh, where the climate fluctuated from extreme cold to extreme heat. Irrespective of the weather, his father would pray every morning for nearly an hour. This had a major bearing on Raman and it led him to meditate on situations, dwell on options and choose the right path at every juncture of his life.

Raman was born into a typical middle class Indian family of the sixties. His father was a civil engineer with one of the public sector undertakings and his mother was a housewife. He had two younger sisters. They all lived in a government quarter provided by his father's firm. It was a modest two bed room house in a typical government housing colony where the neighborhood consisted of families with quite similar backgrounds, beliefs and values. Above all, their common aspiration was that their children should study well because that was the only way forward to a better life.

Since this was a period when there were no TVs, computers, mobile phones, malls or for that matter eating joints, family members had time for each other, and the only way of socializing and entertainment was interaction amongst like-minded families on a regular basis. There would hardly be a day when Raman's family would not visit a family friends' house and vice versa. Because of this regular interaction, family friends in the colony got to know Raman well and considered him a role model for their children because of his academic brilliance, good manners and respect for elders.

As years rolled on and Raman compared his childhood with that of his own children, he discovered that times had changed so much. For instance, some yesteryears' essential items have become obsolete in today's age and time. Some examples are —

1. Inland letters, post cards and telegrams
2. Hold all — An essential while traveling in train. It neatly rolled up mattress, pillow, sheets and blankets.
3. Transistor
4. Indian squat toilet
5. Stove (both kerosene and electrical)
6. Lantern
7. Mosquito net
8. Black and white photographs
9. Hand-knitted sweaters
10. Ink pen
11. Hair ribbons (worn by school girls around their plaits)

And the list goes on...

In Raman's view, Indians can be broadly categorized into three, based on their childhood exposure —

1. Those born before 1955

2. Born between 1955 and 1985

3. Born after 1985

Those born between 1955 and 1985 have grown up in a value-based family environment and witnessed the modernization of India, embracing those changes in to their lives. Those born after 1985 grew up at a time when India was opening up to western influences. India was changing rapidly and so were lifestyles. This was the generation which experienced the outside world via television and internet and matured quickly. In other words, the span of childhood got shortened for this generation. This generation has also not experienced typical Indian values first-hand. The big plus with this generation is that it dares to think out of box.

Raman was born in 1964 and so belonged to the second category. He grew up believing:

1. Hard work is essential in life.

2. One should always be fair.

3. Honesty and integrity cannot be compromised.

4. Self-pride is non-negotiable.

5. Absolute belief in God is a given.

The above values could take strong roots in Raman primarily because of the fact that even though his father was in a position where he could have indulged in corrupt practices, he chose to be absolutely honest in all his professional dealings. Raman remembers one incident when a contractor brought an expensive gold gift for his father and his father politely sent that man out of their house. His father was a hardworking man devoid of any vices.

As a perfect companion to his father, Raman's mother was a simple, highly content house wife who lived her life unconditionally for the happiness of her husband and children.

The tiger lives and dies by the rules. His values are engrained at a very early age. Raman's childhood was shaped by the strong beliefs his father had held and passed on to him. VALUES are the richest legacy we can pass on to the next generation.

———•———

3

PACHMARHI – CIRCA 1974 TO 1980

Raman joined Pachmarhi boarding school in 6th standard. His father's close friend, whom Raman fondly addressed as Ravi uncle, helped them with the admission. Raman's dormitory was for eight students and the facilities were basic with one cot with coir ropes. The first thing he was taught by the boarders was to clean the bugs from the cot and to tighten the ropes to reduce the sagging. Raman also had a small cupboard (3 x 2 feet) along with a desk and a chair. These would be his companions for the next six years.

Unlike his previous school, where he used to take a mat with him to sit on the ground, Kendriya Vidyalaya, Pachmarhi was a slice of heaven. As the majority of students were from an army back ground, the general ambience was far better compared to his past school where his schoolmates were from typically rural back ground. At Pachmarhi, the children were also more articulate and more sophisticated.

However, soon the euphoria came crashing down. The reason was Raman's English, both written and spoken. Though he was a brilliant student (he had topped the district 5th standard board exam and was rewarded with a small bicycle by his father before coming to Pachmarhi), his medium of education had been Hindi. At Pachmarhi, it was English from day one. Hence English was the most dreaded period for poor Raman and Mr. C R Yadav, the English TGT (Trained Graduate Teacher), the most dreaded teacher. Raman felt tormented for weeks.

But Raman had experienced right through his early life that 'when all doors get shut, God opens at least one window!' The boarders were allowed to visit their local guardian every Sunday and on one such visit to Ravi uncle's house, Raman met, to his gleeful surprise, Mr. Yadav, who was enjoying a drink with Uncle Ravi. That very Monday onwards, Raman started enjoying his English classes as Mr. Yadav was more than nice to him now.

EARLY EXPOSURE TO DISCIPLINE

The hostel life was quite regimented. The day would begin at 5am and boarders would have fifteen minutes to change from night suit to Physical Training (PT) uniform and then would be doing 45 minutes of PT, which was primarily stretches followed by a good 5 kilometer run. Once done with PT, the next half an hour was spent in a long queue waiting for the toilet, and then a mad rush to dash in and dash out. The reason being these lavatories were not modern or connected with the sewage line. These were just boxes, bogs which would be emptied and cleaned every day, and invariably by the time one got his turn, these boxes would be overflowing, and smelling of shit, literally! To get over the terrible smell, this would be followed by a quick bath. The bath consisted of one bucket for wetting the body and one for washing away the soap. The main reason for this quickie was the lack of hot water in a cold place like Pachmarhi. Looking back, Raman was happy to have experienced these basic facilities as they made him understand the difficulties common Indians face every day.

With morning chores completed by 6am sharp, the boarders would be at their desk, majority of them only pretending to study. The bell at 7am would be a big relief when they could change into school uniform and, after getting a nod from the Dress captain, rush for breakfast. The very sight of breakfast would be a gastronomical delight as they would be extremely hungry by then.

The classrooms were a five minute walk and while going to school, Raman would watch smartly dressed army officers riding Vespa or Yezdi bikes and dropping their children to school. This scene would form a lump in his throat. He made a silent resolution then that he'll drop and pick his children up from school himself. To this day, Raman makes it a point to do it on as many occasions as possible. After all, 'there is no point having roses in life, if you cannot smell them'.

As school was getting to be fun, Raman's confidence also started building. He was a good looking guy with pleasing manners. Academically, he was brilliant in Mathematics and Hindi and would help other classmates occasionally. This brought him closer to Rashmi who used to sit in the next row. Since it was a co-educational school, boys and girls used to be in the same cohort but sat separately.

The first fall, be it from the bicycle, mango or guava tree, (kids today no longer experience such falls!) or for that matter falling in love, has its own memories. However, considering Raman's age and time, his romance with Rashmi was restricted to sipping water from the common taps during lunch hour and occasionally glancing at each other! This continued for a good three years.

In the 7th standard, Raman came across the librarian, Shukla sir, who for some strange reason took extra interest in him and encouraged his reading habits. By 8th standard, Raman had already read Munshi Premchand, Bankimchand Chatopadhya, Sharad Chandra and other Hindi literature luminaries. English books for his age group were few in the library. It was Shukla sir who also encouraged Raman to participate in debates and extempore speeches. A good teacher's mentoring at an early stage can influence a child immensely throughout his/her life. Raman was extremely indebted to Shukla sir, who helped him blossom into a balanced personality with literary depth.

The boarders used to be back in their hostel by 3pm and next one hour was slotted for letter writing. They had to write three letters compulsorily to their parents every week as there were no phones or email those days. Other evening chores comprised of giving or receiving clothes from the Dhobi (laundry man), and various other mundane activities spiced up by intense discussions on the female anatomy!

Every day, from 4pm to 4.30pm was earmarked for kitchen gardening, where the boys were divided into groups of three to five and were given approximately

5 to 10 sq ft area to grow and tend vegetables of their choice. This exercise bonded them closer with Mother Earth and revealed the mysteries of nature. 4.30 to 6pm was the best part of the day for the boys. It was games time. Kendriya Vidyalaya, Pachmarhi had a very good infrastructure for all the conventional outdoor sports like football, volley ball and cricket. By 6.30pm, the boys would come back to the hostel and by 7pm, they were to be seated at their desks for studies.

Barring half hour from 8pm to 8.30pm which was dinnertime, they were required to remain at their desks till 10 at night. After 9.30pm, it used to become almost impossible to avoid dozing off on their desks. There was also the danger of the prefect or hostel warden taking their nightly rounds. Punishment for falling asleep on the desk included a cold water bath and many other such sadistically novel ideas. At long last, the bell would ring at sharp 10pm. This was the most awaited bell of the day. In less than five minutes, the boarders would dart around to switch off lights and hit the sack. Sleep was also one of the most precious things in Raman's life those days. And though at that time this regimented life was grudgingly accepted, it made Raman a disciplined man.

THE MAKING OF A LEADER

By the time Raman was in the 9th standard, he was undoubtedly the most popular student in the school, well-liked by both students and teachers. He was the uncrowned king of debating and extempore speech, hostel prefect, house captain, volley ball captain, the list was endless. But most importantly, he was kind and genuine in his approach towards everyone. When he reached the 10th standard, a new principal took over the reins. Mr. P.C Sood was a discipline fanatic and in record time earned the distinction of being the most hated person of discussion among the boarders. The final nail in his reputation's coffin was hit when he suspended Raman's three best friends, Ramesh, Rajendran and Raju Mallick for two full days, for a silly reason — bunking one period of Mathematics. To add injury to insult, they were made to line up in front of the principal's office in full public view for the entire day.

A few days before the suspension incident, the school had held its annual function where Raman was awarded the best actor award by the wife of chairman of the board, Colonel Wahi. The Kendriya Vidyalaya, Pachmarhi school management board comprised of senior army officials with the commanding officer as being the chairman. After the suspension incident, Raman's friends suggested that he should go to Colonel Wahi's house and complain against Principal Sood. Raman was beginning to realize that leadership comes at a price. Bravely he made the trip to the chairman's residence and charmed Mrs. Wahi with his innocent looks and endearing stories. The complaints were quite subjective like the food being unpalatable, facilities being unhygienic and so on. The outcome of Raman's initiative was a surprise visit by Colonel Wahi and his team to the hostel, resulting in some much needed improvements — the ancient box type commodes were converted into modern bath and toilet units, coir rope cots were changed to steel framed ones and free supply of meat and milk was ordered from the army to beef up food quality.

Looking back, Raman realized how happy Principal Sood would have been with this complaint of his as the school got a thorough facelift in terms of infrastructure. To give it to the gentleman, Principal Sood went on to improve hostel facilities and enhance standards. He also roped in Maharishi Mahesh Yogi Training Center at Pachmarhi to train boarders in meditation techniques. Raman and other boarders were put under a daily meditation schedule from 6pm to 6.30pm every day, a habit that Raman follows even today. Considering this was in 1978, it demonstrates how ahead of his time Principal Sood was. Before Principal Sood's tenure, Pachmarhi was up to 11th standard. He added 12th standard with Raman's batch being the first one in this new class following the CBSE examination system. Principal Sood's efforts ensured all eleven students in Raman's class passeing with distinction in their CBSE exams.

Another achievement for Principal Sood and particularly for Raman was his admission in IIT (Indian Institute of Technology) Chennai after his 12th. Every year during his childhood till he reached class XII, Raman, along with his parents and sisters, would visit his grandparents who lived in Chennai. During this annual one month visit, Raman would visit IIT play ground almost daily as it was a walking distance from his grandparents' house. He would play mostly with students from IIT or children whose parents were the faculty at IIT. It was this encounter with IIT at an early age which sowed the seeds in Raman to pursue engineering at IIT, and the sound discipline and hard work coupled with efforts of good teachers at Pachmarhi, facilitated his joining IIT Chennai.

Pachmarhi taught Raman:

1. Discipline is very important in day to day life.

2. It is the TEAM and not the individual that matters.

3. Winning is not everything but putting your best effort counts.

4. A LEADER must be reliable, fair and respectable in the eyes of his team members.

5. Life is all about being a good human being.

    Pachmarhi transformed the cub into a young tiger.

———●———

4

EARLY CORPORATE JUNGLE YEARS

Raman was recruited by L&M Company as a graduate engineer trainee or 'GET' during his final year of engineering at IIT Chennai. His first posting was on a highway project near Bangalore. His project was headed by Mr. S K Sharma or SKS, as he was called by colleagues. SKS was an institution within himself. He was the first covenanted officer in L&M. Covenancy was a revered status that was awarded after one cleared a grueling interview with the board. Covenant cadre executives enjoyed lavish perks such as a separate executive bathroom, personal valet and a butler.

SKS was a brilliant engineer, honest to the core and outspoken — always calling a spade a spade. He was one of those officers you either liked or hated but could not ignore. He was also a high performer and had to his credit several prestigious projects. SKS also had the tendency to instantly like or dislike someone. Raman was fortunate to be in the likeable category, thanks to one incident that reinforced it. He was assigned to the quality control department when, one day, his boss was on leave and there was a surprise inspection by the client's chief engineer who was escorted by SKS. Raman was quizzed about the CBR (California bearing ratio — a test for determining quality of soil) value of soil which he answered brilliantly! Raman had incidentally done his project work on this topic and this caught SKS's attention. From then on, he took Raman under his wings and started grooming him.

There were two immediate outcomes of this new found corporate glory. Corporate bosses are such Demi-Gods that if you are in their inner circle, you are envied by one and all. Suddenly people start taking note of you, start flocking around you and you are overwhelmed by the sheer number of parties and other socials you get invited to. This new-found glory can make you a star overnight. However, beneath this entire feel-good facade, the pack of wild dogs starts sniffing around you. Your back is no longer safe now.

L&M those days was one of the very few Indian companies which believed in working hard and partying harder. After days and nights of grueling project schedule, every once a fortnight there would be a dinner party, where the common bridge between the bosses and subordinates would be a generous consumption of free flowing liquor. However there was one catch; the discussions during the party would remain confined to work and the bosses would, next day, remember every word one had spoken the night before!

Mentoring under SKS made Raman a good project manager but also planted the seeds of rock-solid qualities in him like staying honest despite worldly temptations (there were several enticing carrots dangled by vendors and subcontractors), genuinely working hard for the good of the organization, being self-driven, raising the bar and staying away from office politics (the wild dog pack did try to pull him in their fold) and above all, having a heightened sense of self-pride with a tad bit of arrogance in his professional dealings.

Mentoring, which is more of a lip service in today's corporate world, was a real experience in L&M twenty five years back. Raman remembers one particular incident when he was invited by a Professor of Government Engineering College, Bangalore to deliver a lecture on concrete pavements. This invite was the outcome of a visit by the students and faculty of the college to one of Raman's project sites. SKS was delighted and asked Raman to go to L&M headquarters, Chennai and meet Group Head Mr. Subramanian. To his surprise, he was given a 15 minute audience with the group head and was encouraged to go ahead with the university lecture. Though Raman has done more than thousand presentations since then, he still remembers the warmth of those black and white stencils which were created at L &M headquarters.

Mentoring is a very powerful process for any organization and it is also a continuous process. Every successful organization that has withstood the test of time would have mentoring in its DNA and L&M was a classic example of it way back in 80's.

Working with L & M also made Raman's professional foundations very strong. It exposed him to working under well-defined corporate guidelines. The first long standing job and boss play a very important role in shaping the future of a professional. It either encourages him to be a tiger or become a member of the pack in time.

His mentor's powerful influence made sure that Raman grew into a full-grown tiger in the corporate jungle. Neither SKS nor Raman had any clue that over time, wild dog packs would become so vicious and powerful in society that being a tiger would be a nightmarish experience. (You would have heard of the recent ADARSH society scam in Mumbai that involved packs even from the Defense services, which is supposed to be the least corrupt amongst organizations with high morals).

———•———

5

THE BEGINNING OF A
NEW ERA

Though Raman was on the fast track at L&M (with three promotions in a row), he was made aware of his higher growth potential by his close peer group, Kulkarni, Harish and Ravi. They assured him that they, as a team under his leadership, would be able to achieve much more and much bigger things in life. Their conversations over pitchers of beer and kebabs were a laughter cocktail with lethal digs at lesser mortals in the company and how way below those chaps were. One of the prime reasons for this group's arrogance was Raman's proclaimed proximity to the super boss SKS. After all, power in any form is intoxicating.

After being with L&M for almost five years, Raman decided to quit one fine morning. This syndrome hits high performers in large, structured companies and typically surfaces between 3 to 5 years of service. The key reason behind this is that high caliber professionals get bored with the day-to-day mundane work culture very soon. That is why many companies now have fast track growth paths for exceptional individuals so that the wheat is separated from the chaff.

On hearing about Raman's resignation, SKS was fuming and refused to talk to him for a week. However his friends admired his courage and the pack of wild dogs were relieved that they had to contend with one less tiger.

Around the same time, Raman was blessed with a baby girl. After a short stint of two years with a company in the Middle East, Raman was back in Bombay where his wife Meera was holding a job and their baby daughter was now two years old. Within a month, Raman got a job with cement major ABC. In the mid-nineties, forward and backward integration of core business was the buzz word and in the case of ABC, the Managing Director was driving it personally through Dr. Anil Kumar or AKC, the Executive Director.

CONCRETE CHANGE

Dr. AKC was a visionary and under his leadership ABC decided to foray into the business of building materials like ready mixed concrete. A new business vertical was formed to take the ready mixed concrete business forward. Being a newly created vertical, several internal strings were being pulled by various aspirants within the company to spearhead the initiative. As luck would have it, through a chance meeting that lasted just a few minutes, Dr. AKC selected Raman to head this new vertical. Doesn't everything good in life come with a catch? His unit was to be based in Bangalore. After intense discussions with the family, it was decided that Meera would quit her comfortable job in Bombay and they would all move to Bangalore. It's a well-established fact that a man's biggest support in his professional life is his wife. She can play the pivotal role in shaping a man's career.

Raman and family moved to Bangalore in 1994 and Raman took to his job like fish to water. He had all the ingredients of an entrepreneur and also had the solid backing of his super boss, Dr. AKC.

The building material industry in particular and concrete industry in general was at a nascent stage in mid-nineties. Concrete was made at site by mixing cement, sand and aggregate plus water and though the strength of a building was provided by concrete, the entire process of making concrete was very primitive. This wasn't the case in advanced countries. There, since early sixties, concrete making was carried out in a factory setup under stringent quality norms which included mixing the right proportion of cement and water. Concrete made this way would give long life to a structure.

Concrete is one of those materials which has scope for huge anomalies, sometimes with very tragic consequences. The biggest abuse comes from the amount of cement that is mixed in concrete. During the nineties, India was producing around a hundred million tons of cement. On a conservative estimate, this would translate to 150 million cubic meter of concrete, making concrete industry worth a whooping Rupees 25,000 crore! Because of the size of this business and with cement being the most expensive material in the mix, contractors/builders would use less cement to enhance their profit margins. With this ground reality, ABC was pioneering the first commercial ready mix concrete plant in India at Bangalore during mid-nineties. It was therefore normal to face opposition from vested interest groups. This time, the resistance was more than normal and went to the extent of Raman receiving threatening calls. But the tiger in Raman refused to budge and continued to fight it out. The journey was difficult but in time, things started to look better as any change whose time has come, gets the support of cosmic forces that ensure its success. In less than two years, Raman and his company's initiative started showing results and also started attracting competition. The biggest competition came from a Singapore based corporate giant called Supernova corporation. Supernova, the biggest building material company in Singapore today, was then looking at the Indian market, post the economic liberalization of the early nineties.

One morning, Mr. Ben, the Managing Director of Supernova, India, visited Raman at his factory on the outskirts of Bangalore. They went around the unit and Raman did his best to impress Ben. Ben listened intently and absorbed all the data. As days went by, Raman forgot this incident. Then, few weeks later, Ben invited him for a drink. They met at a pub and Raman was thus introduced to Kelvin, his future boss, who would groom him to be a full grown tiger in the years to come.

Kelvin was a tall, well-built man with blonde hair and drooping moustache. His body language was close to being intimidating but Kelvin and Raman got along like a house on fire. And as Kelvin put it later, "We both were hustlers."

A week after this informal meeting, Raman received a call from a Sanjay Chakraborty who said that he would like to meet him and discuss an opportunity that would be profitable to Raman. They decided to meet at the Bangalore Club where this guy disclosed to Raman that he was actually the head of a recruiting firm and was there on behalf of Supernova to invite him to come on their Board. This was an all-new experience compared to attending formal interviews and interacting with condescending HR guys scanning the CV and trying hard negotiations. Way back in nineties, this approach of Sanjay's was very different from what Raman had dealt with till then. Sanjay also stressed upon the fact that Supernova had zeroed in on Raman, after a country-wide search, including the conventional newspaper advertisement route. After another round of drinks, he also mentioned that the cost to company in the offing was excellent. Raman had no clue of cost to company at that stage of his career; he only knew gross and net salary. After this meeting, Raman left the club in a state of euphoria, disbelief and confusion.

The next few days were spent in talking to friends, well-wishers and of course, his wife Meera. The most common opinion was that 'you never know these multinationals; they could wind up one fine morning'. ABC had a nice guest house at Ooty and Raman had requested for a booking some time back. Precisely at this stage of confusion, he was told the guest house had become available due to some cancellations.

So Raman, Meera and Ramya, their daughter, had a whale of a time at a highly subsidized cost (a three star room at Rs 10 a day and food at actual). They would have merely spent around Rs 1000 for their comfortable seven days' stay. Raman firmly believed that any major decision in life should be taken in a good surrounding, preferably away from the routine. And the fresh air of Ooty helped clear Raman's mind on the Supernova's offer. After reaching Bangalore, Raman called up Sanjay and informed him of his decision to join Supernova Corporation.

WORKING WITH A MULTINATIONAL — A PARADIGM SHIFT

Raman's first official meeting with Kelvin had starting trouble. For the first few months, Supernova India operated out of a Business Centre on MG Road, Bangalore. On his first day, Raman was supposed to report at 9am. Like any typical Indian executive, he reached seven minutes late. Kelvin had a very expressive face and the anger was writ all over it. His first sentence was, "Not acceptable. If you want to work for me you have to be on time and let's tune our watches so as to minimize any confusion."

He was also ready with Raman's employment offer along with the job description. This was all French to Raman as he had never been exposed to such structured induction. Kelvin patiently read out the entire document for Raman and explained wherever necessary. When Raman had the contract in hand, he couldn't believe the number of zeros against his salary. Kelvin also showed Raman a couple of corporate films and emphasized heavily on health and safety, integrity

(Singapore being amongst the least corrupt countries in the world) and concepts like team building and leadership.

After the initial glitch, the rest of the morning went really well. The biggest surprise was, when they broke for lunch, Kelvin took out a bunch of keys and wished Raman 'Happy Motoring'. Here was a brand new four wheel drive Maruti Gypsy for him. He and Kelvin went out on an inaugural drive and Raman was on cloud nine by now!

Post lunch, Kelvin took Raman to Ben, who in turn explained to him their Indian business plan for the next five years. It was done in great detail. Towards the end of his first day at SUPERNOVA, two things drew Raman's attention:

1. Both Ben and Kelvin were prepared thoroughly for market entry and a lot of ground work had been done meticulously, unlike the casual approach he had witnessed so far on his first day at previous jobs. First day at college or at work (in any position) is very critical for an individual and it's a pity that majority of indigenous organizations and business leaders do not give it much thought or attention.

2. The day was well-structured even though it appeared spontaneous. The time spent was totally qualitative and participative. Raman was made to feel comfortable, even while expressing

his disagreement. Kelvin explained to him that there should always be an open discussion in a closed room and not vice versa.

It would be anybody's guess as to how many Kelvins and Bens are around in today's business world.

KELVIN — THE REAL MENTOR

Kelvin's day at RMC plant would begin at 8am though the official working hours were from 9am to 6pm and he was totally hands on. He started his career as a truck driver and went on to become a director. The entire plant construction at Whitefield (on the outskirts of Bangalore) was spearheaded by him. Once everything was ready for the trial production, Raman asked Kelvin how many labourers would be required to lay the trial concrete. Pat came his reply, "You, Ben and me." The next day itself, the three of them lay concrete with their own hands. There were two reasons for Kelvin to do this. He felt that one must have a first-hand feel of the product one deals with and secondly, any start up business must have team effort to bring in the cohesion in the team.

Kelvin deliberately shared his office with Raman for three good years and groomed, kicked, nurtured, taught and mentored him rigorously. He was committed, focused on business needs, a fair boss, enthusiastic team player and a wonderful human being. He taught Raman so much on how to build an organization. In his view, any organization could do well if it is built properly with the right set of people. He was a firm believer of 'birds of a feather flock together'. Building good organizations begin with simple things like interviewing which should have the following guidelines.

INTERVIEWING TECHNIQUES

1. Stick to time.
2. Be prepared.
3. Be courteous (an interview is another form of fact-finding, not interrogation).
4. While assessing, focus on values like integrity, customer focus and team play in the candidate.
5. Give a balanced brief of the organization in terms of its strengths and weaknesses.
6. Be transparent with remuneration (Kelvin's favourite dialogue was 'Pay peanuts, and get monkeys').
7. Lastly, inform the candidates about selection or rejection within the committed time frame.

It's an established fact that many HR professionals would not carry out even half of the above fundamentals and this was precisely the reason Supernova believed that what HR does can be better performed by the manager himself. Controversial, but that's why Supernova-India never had a Human Resource department. When Raman heard this concept first, he thought it was absurd. Today, after more than a decade, he is totally convinced that HR should be a line manager's role, because one cannot outsource his talent issues, and the biggest challenge for any manager is recruiting the right talent. Supernova also used 360 degree review, which in Raman's mind is the best tool to check complacency, especially among senior managers, and stimulate professional development.

Another culture at Supernova was 'multi-tasking' or deploying multiple skills. Kelvin could drive a wheel loader, batch concrete, operate a transit mixer truck (that carries concrete) as well as operate a concrete pump. And he made sure everyone learnt as much as possible about different aspect of business, from sales, technical to operations. Multi-tasking as a rule should be part of ever individual's repertoire. This helps an organization to remain lean and effective.

Supernova also believed in direct employment of employees at all levels, including drivers, which is a rare practice with corporates. Both Ben and Kelvin were very clear that a driver, who spends maximum time at site with customer, would give his best only if he is taken care of by the company equally well. Supernova also brought the best of plant and machinery to India and thus demonstrated its long term approach to business.

Supernova products were at par with world standards and hence were expensive. This in turn put sales under pressure because its offering of ready mix concrete was almost 20% more expensive than normal concrete, due largely to manufacturing and transportation costs and an additional 10% excise duty. Kelvin was against any price cut, as he firmly believed in selling ready mix on merit alone. So Raman and team were selling a product which was quite expensive. Moreover, Supernova, following its long term goals, had set up a unit which was world-class but idling, waiting for order bookings. This was putting Raman under severe pressure and he would tell his wife at times, that soon enough the Singaporeans would have to shut the shop and leave. But the Singaporeans knew very well what they were pursuing.

Kelvin as a boss was not only a pusher, he provided solutions too. After studying the Bangalore market for a while, he advised Raman and team to focus on individual households. During those days, it was typical of Bangaloreans to own independent houses rather than buying readymade flats. The owner would prefer to directly buy high quality product from Supernova unlike a contractor or a builder, who would not bother much about quality. The identification of this segment of individual owners was difficult as it was spread across fifty square kilometers or more. Also the customer in this segment was very demanding. Raman recollects one incident when due to some unavoidable circumstance one dispatch of roof concreting was delayed. The irate customer called up Supernova head office in Singapore, and put everyone in Bangalore to task!

But as Supernova in India had no option but to succeed, the entire Bangalore team i.e. sales, technical, operations and accounts was mobilized for this challenge. For instance, the receptionist was supposed to answer the call within three rings. Kelvin also believed in punctuality and therefore Supernova's trucks would reach any site dot on, at the appointed time. Raman too had spent nights on site ensuring timely delivery. This unrelenting hard work gave Supernova good word of mouth publicity and it did not have to resort to expensive promotional jamborees.

In a few months, the sales figures were looking good with more than 75% revenues coming from individual household segment. This segment also did not require credit facilities. While servicing this segment, Raman realized that building a home is very close to the customers' hearts and he was extremely fortunate that he was a part of this experience. So close was the bonding that before starting the concreting, his trucks would be worshiped and once Raman was asked to share food from the common plate of trustees who were building a religious structure. This was quite an honour! These moments brought a sense of moral responsibility and for Raman business became more than just sales and number game. Even today Raman's chest swells with pride when he sees these structures standing strong in and around Bangalore. He recollects with fondness and pride those nights, standing tirelessly for hours to get the concreting done.

THE 8 O'CLOCK SALES MEETING

Kelvin believed in the 'KISS' principle of keeping it simple and straight in business. One of his practices which Raman still follows is the morning sales meetings. The rules of this meeting are very basic and are as follows:

1. The meeting starts at sharp 8 o'clock (in some exceptional cases 8.30am but no later than that). It is chaired by Raman himself.

2. The meeting revolves around short term, immediate objectives.

3. If required, the meeting is attended by operation, technical and accounts. This ensures that there is no passing the buck, and sales guys don't have the excuse of 'internal issues'.

4. The meeting gets over by 9am. Long meetings are always counterproductive.

5. The meeting concludes with definite ACTIVITIES and not promises/hopes of expected results.

Though at Supernova, these morning meetings were a regular affair, it is suggested that this tool is used on a case-to-case basis by organizations. There is no doubt that such meetings, conducted on a regular basis, can change the performance of any organization anywhere in the world.

Kelvin was also a strong believer of 'walking the talk'.

Raman remembers one incident when they had just finished the supply of concrete to one particular project when the site engineer pointed out to him that they had supplied a lower quality material. Raman checked with the plant and was told that they had indeed made a mistake. Since there was short supply of concrete of the required quality, his operations and technical managers suggested that he should try to cover it up by saying that whatever was mentioned in the delivery note was a typographical error. Raman would have done that but for the fear of Kelvin. It was six in the morning and he knew that Kelvin's previous night's hangover would still be lingering, but still he mustered the courage and called up explaining the situation. Kelvin heard Raman patiently and just said, "Up front it," and hung the phone. Raman thought this gora (foreigner) is out of his head but Kelvin was the boss and Raman had no choice but to tell the truth to the customer.

Later, over a mug of beer, Kelvin explained to him that if he wanted to build an organization of integrity and ethical practices and also an organization which would never cheat its customers, then the values must be inculcated internally first, among the employees. In this particular case, many people in the company knew that Supernova had made a mistake with the wrong grade/type of concrete, and covering it up would have lead to a major setback for the company in the long run.

Now this is what is called integrity of character. Unfortunately there is lack of business leaders like Kelvin in today's world. Today's business leaders would often go to any length to cover up all wrong doings and when it comes to customers, they would choose the short and easy path.

Kelvin also believed in bonding beyond the sphere of regular work. Every alternate Saturday, he and Raman would hit the pub and play snooker. At times they would be joined by Kelvin's wife Roma, who was a wonderful support. Raman recollects one evening when he was feeling down and Roma saw it in his face and said, "Raman, it's difficult to keep pace with my husband but believe me he would bail you out when you are in neck deep shit."

Roma and Kelvin were a wonderful couple and Roma was married to Kelvin and his work both, equally. She would ensure that every time she came back from Singapore, she would bring gifts for Raman's wife Meera and both their daughters. She was also instrumental in building a beautiful rock garden at the Supernova India's factory which she did all by herself, with a bit of support from the drivers.

Kelvin and Roma loved India genuinely and were quite popular in the Bangalore social circuit. When they went back to Singapore, they took one container full of souvenirs which also included a bullock cart which

Kelvin converted into an open air bar in his garden. After starting their first unit at Bangalore, Supernova quickly moved to set up their second unit, south of Bangalore and a third one at Hyderabad. Thanks to Kelvin's understanding of market growth, these units, even decades later, have commercial viability.

By early 2000, as per a business survey, Supernova was an established market leader in the ready mixed concrete business in India. But for Supernova, the ready mixed concrete industry would not have seen growth in India, especially in south India. Supernova set the industry benchmark.

Raman's tenure at Supernova was the best part of his life. He was so obsessed with his work that he had celebrated a few New Year eves and many other nights, along with his family and friends, at his factory. There would be numerous occasions when Raman would take his wife and daughter out on the pretext of a drive at night, to a construction site where Supernova would be supplying concrete, just to get a first-hand feel of customer satisfaction.

A good organization is all about creating passion among employees and Kelvin was a master at this. Kelvin left India in 2001 and with his departure Raman's good time with Supernova also started coming to an end. Supernova, as a company was going through a rough phase globally and the primary reason for this was their venture in the Chinese steel market which had backfired badly. The board decided one fine morning that except Singapore operations, all other regions would be closed or scaled down. This came as a rude shock for Raman and also made him realize that corporate life could be a roller-coaster.

Supernova decided to sell off Indian business, which though successful in a short span of time was very small in the larger scale of things. Though this information was kept a well-guarded secret, Raman was privy to this top secret.

The Supernova tenure made Raman a full grown corporate tiger with all the right attributes in place.

———•———

6

KELVIN'S PRIMARY TO MIKE'S SECONDARY

AMC Gmbh, Germany was the largest supplier of building materials in the world during the nineties. AMC also had ventured into the Indian market around the same time as Supernova.

Mr. Mike, a British, was the CEO of AMC when Raman met him in mid 2000. Mike, a clever team builder, was quick to drop hints, for a job opportunity, to Raman, which Raman readily accepted as he was aware of internal turbulence at Supernova. Raman was hired as Regional General Manager, South and since

AMC had business interest only in Hyderabad, he moved to Hyderabad along with his family in Mid-Dec 2002. Hyderabad and Bangalore are two entirely different cities culture-wise and Raman's family could not adjust to Hyderabad at all. So in three months flat, they decided to shift back to Bangalore.

Working for AMC was entirely different from Supernova. Supernova had hands-on approach to business with more focus on micro issues whereas AMC by virtue of its global presence had a more corporate and systematic way of doing things. In AMC, the top structure started as functional roles and later changed to profit centre heads, whereas Supernova operated on a profit centre head approach from the beginning. Supernova had their corporate office at the plant, whereas AMC had a corporate address. The net result was that, at the end of five year of inception, AMC was losing money and Supernova was making money! 'Any business is all about being connected at the grass root level' and Kelvin and Ben were masters in it.

Mike had a background of turning around businesses and was sent to India with this particular mandate by AMC Gmbh bosses. He had also run aggregate and quarrying business earlier and was keen on managing a start-up in India. Somehow, he was able to acquire a decent crusher and quarry at the outskirts of Hyderabad and was determined to make this unprofitable venture successful. This was a new business for Raman, and

Mike, another tiger to the core with better maneuvering skills for corporate world, loved teaching the nitty-gritty of aggregate business to Raman. He also got Raman enrolled for a two year distance learning course in Mining and Crushing with a reputed Mining Institute in Australia.

If Kelvin was Raman's high school teacher, Mike was his college professor.

Raman, by now, had a brilliant reputation in the ready mixed concrete industry, especially in the Bangalore market and the tiger in him was confident of turning around business of AMC at Hyderabad also. But very soon, he realized that in India, everything changes every 150 kilometers, especially the way business is conducted.

The AMC team at Hyderabad was lacking direction and motivation. It was an army full of Generals and with hardly any soldiers on ground. Raman decided to spend more time with the customers than at the office. Before he could even settle down, the first casualty of a new assignment came knocking, when Kishore, the sales manager at AMC, resigned. Raman tried hard to persuade him but realized that he was vying in vain for Raman's position. His exit created another problem. He was joining a competitor and apart from the knowledge and experience he was carrying, he was also taking a few AMC employees with him. On hearing this, Mike immediately flew down to Hyderabad and helped

Raman tide over this problem. Raman learned a major lesson from Mike's arrival, that at any crucial juncture, a leader must ensure that he is physically present to support his team and doesn't just motivate them by 'MBT' or 'Management by Talking' from a distance. (Unfortunately several CEOs do this today.) In fact, with the advent of mobile technology, they feel that they would be wasting their as well as subordinates' time by travelling and therefore, resort to giving sermons on the phone which, truly speaking, do not help much in times of crisis.

Mike was different and he made Raman realize that every successful organization should have leaders who lead from the front. THINKER FINISHER leaders of the organizations are the need of the hour.

THINKER FINISHER

A thinker finisher is the one who is not only good at strategy formulation, but also takes it to logical conclusion by executing it.

Characteristics of a Thinker Finisher:
1. Understands his current role critically.
2. Understands his contribution to business clearly.
3. Understands limitations of organizations and market.
4. Understands business-related numbers.
5. Visualizes the scalability.

The Making of a Thinker Finisher:

1. Prioritizes his objectives in line with business needs.
2. Divides them into short/medium/long term time frame.
3. Collects data (internally & externally) including numbers and draws baseline based on that.
4. Thinks over objectives in a structured manner.
5. Draws list of activities.
6. Executes activities in a regimented manner.
7. Leads from the front.
8. Remains empathetic/sympathetic to the team.
9. Resolves road blocks regularly.
10. Remains rigid and also flexible with objectives.
11. Celebrates milestones.
12. Continues team building.
13. Reviews and revisits periodically.
14. Sets a new benchmark.

In Mike's view, Mahatma Gandhi was the greatest Thinker Finisher ever because he devised a strategy against the British rule and took it to its logical conclusion in the form of gaining independence for India.

As a CEO, Mike also initiated a few innovative

management techniques. One of them was 'COMMUNICATION FORUM', where he would interact with a group of employees from various departments/levels in the absence of their bosses. This would encourage them to speak out about genuine issues minus politics. This way of reaching out to employees by top management is very essential because by mingling with the bottom of the chain employees, a lot can be understood. But unfortunately not many CEOs would do this today. On the contrary, the higher you go in an organization, the more inaccessible you become to your very own people.

Mike used to say, "If you want to go to heaven, you have to die first," which implied that there is nothing like remote control management. AMC crusher and quarry was on the outskirts of Hyderabad and the approach road was terrible. The first thing Mike would do after landing in Hyderabad is, head straight to the quarry and then in the searing hot weather of Hyderabad, change into safety shoes, helmet and safety jacket and walk 5 kilometers around the quarry. This would be followed by a master class on benching, wagon drilling, control blasting, blast size, crusher output, product profile, maintenance schedule and more. He would also ensure that he interacted with every workman during his visit. He would conclude his visit with a dinner meeting with Raman where he would listen intently. Listening skills in today's corporate world are very hard to find, especially when the corporate leaders are used to shouting from the roof tops or engaging in MBT (Management by Talking).

India produces close to a thousand million tons of aggregate for making concrete alone and if you add another 50,000,000 (Five hundred million) of aggregate for various another applications, the aggregate industry stands at a staggering Rs.150,000,000,000 (One hundred and fifty thousand million). Unfortunately, more than 95% of it is in the hands of disorganized players with not much concern for safety, welfare and statutory requirement. In many places, the operations are illegal and controlled by local mafias. Mike and Raman were able to set ethical standards against this back drop.

Some of the innovative measures they were able to implement successfully were:

1. Controlled wagon drill blasting with minimum fly rocks, thus ensuring the safety of nearby villagers.

2. Mechanized operations with state of the art machines requiring minimum workforce.

3. Using fogging techniques to minimize dust emissions.

4. Awarding production linked incentives to workers for working efficiently and safely without any accidents.

5. Providing customers with a copy of royalty challan (fee) paid to the government, a copy of test certificate ensuring quality, and authentic weighment slip (the material was sold in tons rather than in cubic feet, an age old dubious practice where the truck measurement was done manually and could be subjective).

6. Restoration work, including tree plantation around quarries.

7. Launching community schemes like free distribution of school note books, street lights, drinking water facilities around the villages.

Mike also taught Raman, how to be a leader and not just a manager. He sharpened the following qualities in him:

1. Integrity
2. Passion for work
3. Listening, not just hearing
4. Reasoning and calm judgment
5. Firm but fair
6. Proactive and not reactive
7. Eye for detail including number-analysis
8. Thinking global and acting local

Mike's grooming made Raman a savvy and mature corporate tiger.

———•———

7

WHAT MAKES A TIGER
THE LORD OF THE JUNGLE

A tiger has the following distinct characteristics:

1. **Whiskers** — Vibrissae or tactile hairs grow in three different parts of the body and can grow up to 15cm. These are used to track prey by sniffing for ground odour.

2. **Hearing** — Tigers have such an amazing sense of hearing that they can very easily distinguish between the rustle of leaves and a prey. They can also distinguish between sounds made by different herds of animals and can plan their attack in a concerted manner. They can also

identify the noise of a rifle being loaded, a twig crunching beneath a human foot or the breath of a man camouflaged somewhere. They also have white spots or flashes at the back of their ear which appear as illusory eyes to fool their prey or to discourage predators who may normally hunt and attack from behind.

3. **Eye sight** — Tigers have circular pupils and yellow irises. Due to lack of cones in their eye, they see more of depth than color. Tigers have the brightest pair of eyes amongst all animals. They also have wide angle view but all of this with one huge disadvantage. They cannot see a stationary object even if it is as close as five meters. Fortunately for the tiger, other animals become so nervous in its presence, that they start moving and the smallest twitch is enough for the tiger to spot its prey.

THE CHARACTERISTICS OF A WILD DOG PACK

Wild dog packs are found in almost all organizations. In most cases, like the wild dogs, the corporate wild dogs maintain a low or a camouflaged profile and sighting them or identifying them is always a tough task.

THE CORE OF THE TEAM

The nucleus of the pack would have a master manipulator or the leader. Invariably, this guy would be in a position of authority, if not possessing absolute authority in the organization. He would have a few trusted core members around.

The other members consist of:

1. Premium membership of a closed group

In most work places in India, your surname creates your first impression. Over the years, Raman has seen that people connect better if they speak the same language. It gives them the comfort of speaking to someone who hails from a similar background and culture. In other words, someone they can depend upon, in the ever changing, highly competitive corporate atmosphere. This syndrome is more common with old hands in an organization and at times you may feel invisible when members of the pack are happily communicating with each other in their mother tongue, totally oblivious of your presence. Common language is one of the strongest bonding factors in the pack and most often, the master manipulator would be speaking this common language.

2. Symbiosis

Today's corporate world is all about gains. These gains could be in terms of:

1. Good profile
2. Overseas trip
3. Promotion

4. Information sharing

5. Monetary benefits

The list is endless and could contain even trivial items, such as choice of airlines, premium operators vis-à-vis low cost ones. The members of the pack would happily exchange benefits and gains within their closed group but would give trouble to those who were outside their group and were perceived to have tigerly qualities.

This symbiotic give and take works as a very strong glue in keeping the pack together.

3. Temporary membership

Corporate wild dog packs, like clubs, also have some temporary members who are invited from time to time by the master manipulator or core members. These members are included for specific actions against the tiger and his team and if found effective, their membership is extended. Temporary membership is also used as a taster session or bait to lure future pack members.

4. Functional abilities

The biggest strength of a wild dog pack is its ability to perform in a highly coordinated and focused manner. Raman was not able to take his mind off from the scene witnessed at Madumalai. The intensity and brutality of dogs and the helplessness of the mother bison was still fresh in his mind. On a one to one basis, a wild dog is too timid against a huge animal like the bison but it was their combined force which was making all the difference that day.

Raman also recollected the forest guard telling him that the dogs must have prepared for days or weeks together to launch this kind of attack. A lot of effort would have gone into it, collecting data, tracking bison herd movement, identifying the number of calves, streamlining potential areas of attack and identifying the role of each member in detail. Besides, they would have kept a contingency plan ready too.

The corporate wild dog pack would also have the following functional roles to launch an effective collective attack on the tiger and his team members:

1. Master manipulator – The big boss.

2. The sniffer cell (colleagues from Finance and Accounts for instance) – They would get information by being friendly with the tiger and his team.

3. The propagandist (people normally from HR and Purchase functions) – To bad-mouth the tiger and his team. The pack would work on the premise that a well-spread rumor has the potential of becoming truth.

4. Trouble shooters (people normally from Administrative functions) – For dousing any fire

which could cause damage to the master manipulator.

5. Fixers (normally functional heads) — To settle ruffled feathers caused by the tiger. The wild dogs strongly believe in 'shooting the messenger'.

6. Hackers (typically IT guys) — They would hack the tiger and his followers' emails and telephone conversations.

7. Opportunists (normally non-performing functional heads who would struggle to get a job elsewhere) — They are used for specific roles against the tiger.

8 The Barkers (people from Accounts and HR) — They create road blocks and irritants for the tiger and his team.

9. The Nibblers (mainly drivers, office boys, security guards etc) — They provide tit-bits to the manipulator.

10. The Charmers (normally from Sales and Front Desk) — A kill is always easier with the fairer sex on your side and the master manipulator knows it too well.

———•———

8

THE CLASH OF THE WILD DOGS AND THE TIGER

Raman had learnt over the years that one's success rate was directly proportional to the sniffing by the pack. One of the Sniffer in AMC was Chaila who was from Finance and Administration and from the very first day, reminded Raman of his classmate at school, who would derive a sadistic pleasure in complaining about good students with a view to tar their reputation.

After Raman took charge at Hyderabad, the company reported a notional profit in the very third month, (for the first time in the three year history of establishing business in Hyderabad). Raman and his team were ecstatic about it. However, through his crafty accounting skills, Chaila made sure they continued to be in red, by a mere 5000 rupees! The bottom line of any company can be twisted by the view taken by the Accounts guys. This was quite a surprise and a rude shock for Raman and team. Looking back, Raman wishes he had picked up the signals sooner. The second signal was evident when Raman had to ask Satish, his quarry manager to leave the company on a very trivial issue, again courtesy Chaila. Satish had to buy a few urgent spares, without which the operation would have stopped. He decided to buy it from the advance given by a customer and genuinely forgot to ratify it quickly with Raman. This was secretly fed to Chaila by one of the local accounts guys and he made a big issue out of it ensuring that Satish lost his job thus handicapping Raman and his quarry business which was shaping out well by then.

Raman realized quickly that as a rule, the wild dogs first attack people around the tiger before attacking the tiger himself. Also as Raman would learn later, Chaila was only a front man, duly controlled by the master manipulator of the pack.

AMC started its Bangalore operations in late 2004. Raman's next year was spent shuttling between Bangalore and Hyderabad as he continued to be based in Hyderabad.

As far as Bangalore operations were concerned, Raman also faced the trauma of competing against his previous company Supernova, which he had built with blood and sweat a few years back. He tried not to poach any one from Supernova, as he believed that one must always have respect and gratitude towards all the 'ex-es'. Role-wise, he was back to his early days of Supernova, building the AMC Bangalore operation from scratch. As he got ready to start, he got the third signal from the wild dog pack and this time, it came loud and clear from the very top, the Master Manipulator or Baba, who was then the chief operating officer, next only to Mike. He imposed upon Raman a guy from Bombay to head Bangalore business. Even though Mike also seemed not very happy with this choice, he could do nothing and Raman had to agree to this member of the pack whose only credentials were his loyalty to Baba.

WILD CORPORATE DOGS

Raman recollected meeting Naren, the head of Technical at AMC, at a conference while he was still at Supernova. Naren was technically very sound and a brilliant marketing professional. Naren incidentally was also a polished, well-groomed tiger. By the time Raman joined AMC, Baba and Chaila had established themselves in the company and had already started working on recruiting members for the pack. They also ensured that Naren was projected as a sound theoretical man to Mike. If you have the concurrence of a few colleagues' in the corporate world, you can create a completely false perception about an individual and turn a lie in to a gospel truth. Baba was a champion of this game and played it very well against Naren.

Mike left India in April 2004 and the reins of the AMC business was handed over to Baba. One major reason for this was the fact that AMC believed in seniority and Baba was the senior-most manager, if not the most deserving. Baba was well-qualified, intelligent, mild-mannered, would keep his mouth shut most times and above all, was brilliant at masking his character. It was extremely difficult to know his true colours on the surface of his mask and he was more suited as a politician than a technocrat. He was fully aware that he had reached his position by default and thus was fiercely protective of it. Therefore, like the majority of Indian politicians, Baba was extremely focused on retaining his position, by hook or by crook. Right after Mike's departure, Baba swung into action. The first thing he focused on was to get his loyal people into his senior management team; people he could rely upon. He knew for sure that Naren, a more competent guy, could be a threat to him at any given time. He also knew that with Raman's credentials, he should also be kept in check. A new guy, Ajay was hurriedly recruited from a completely different industry to head their quarry business and the reason cited was that the company needed a person exclusively to focus on this business (incidentally the very first task carried out by Ajay, with due support from Baba and Chaila, was to cancel the lease agreement of the Hyderabad quarry). With Mike long gone, Raman's quarry and crusher experience and the efforts at Hyderabad, and the prestigious course from the Australian Institute, had no takers.

Baba also played another masterly stroke in a short span. He asked Raman to concentrate only on their Bangalore business. Raman, till then as GM-South was looking after both Bangalore and Hyderabad operations stationed out of Hyderabad. Baba, knowing Raman's fondness for Bangalore, offered to shift his base to Bangalore, positioning it as a favor. Raman took the bait, little realizing then what he was getting himself into. And soon after this, Baba completed his game plan by asking Naren to look after Hyderabad as an additional responsibility, fully aware that work wise it would be difficult for Naren to do justice to this role as he had an all-India technical role and was based in Mumbai. Baba and Chaila, along with a few others in the pack, made sure that with this new role, Naren's life became a mess and also left no stone unturned to constantly harass him professionally and personally. Raman remembers one incident when one of Chaila's right-hand men, one of the barker wild dogs, an Accounts guy, almost humiliated Naren for a minor totaling mistake of Rs.331 in a non-descript travel expense claim. It is a different story that this barker, later made an excess payment of Rs.35 lakhs to a vendor, which couldn't be recovered and no action was taken against him.

The strategy against Naren paid off and AMC lost the best technical hand in the country. This also had a cascading effect. Along with Naren, some talented technical hands also left AMC and all the hard work in Technical department including the smooth-running technical systems just went down the drain. Looking back, Raman has no doubt in his mind that if Naren had succeeded Mike, not just AMC but the entire Indian ready mixed concrete industry would have been different today.

(Naren joined as Managing Director of an Italian multinational and took it to greater heights in due course).

THE RISE OF THE PACK

Two major events occurred in 2005:

1. Raman lost his father in August
2. AMC acquired Supernova-India

The first incident devastated Raman personally and the second incident derailed his professional growth.

The due diligence for the Supernova-India sale to AMC took almost a year and the Supernova acquisition opened new avenues for AMC in general and Baba in particular. Now Baba had a big pool of talent available to him. The first thing he did was to keep Raman at bay even though he was the best man available to instill synergy during the merger. By doing this, Baba was also sending signals to potential members of the pack to join him.

Mr. Opportunist was a manager at Supernova and his only grouse against Raman was his relatively low salary or CTC at Supernova during Raman's tenure. In every organization, however hard one tries, people come to know about others' salaries. This knowledge gets further reinforced during increment time when people get unhappy about what others have got. Mr. Opportunist had all the ingredients of a pack member and was able to sniff the direction of the wind quickly. He became Baba's right hand man during the merger and was suitably rewarded from time to time. However, to be fair to him, it was actually Baba who exploited him by luring him to become a temporary member of the pack, which unfortunately many people like Mr. Opportunist, in the corporate jungle, never realize. And like trade unions, the route to pack is only one way, 'Once you get in, you cannot get out'.

After the merger, AMC achieved sizable presence in the south and for Raman's credentials, experience and as Regional General Manager, South he should have been the ideal candidate for the merged entity. But

Baba, who had improvised his skills by now, came out with another theory. He insisted that the combined presence of AMC and Supernova was quite sizeable at Bangalore and the only person who could derive the best mileage from this merger was Raman. So he sold Raman the idea that it was not important how big the plate was but more importantly how full the plate was. Sadly today's people management in the corporate sector is often more about effective packaging, and presenting lies as truth.

Raman was re-designated as Regional General Manager, Karnataka and to balance the equation, the position of Regional General Manager, Andhra Pradesh was created for which Mr. Opportunist was duly elevated and sent to Hyderabad. The immediate fall out of this was the loss of Hyderabad Business Head, Akash, a brilliant guy from Supernova, who left AMC immediately and joined a start-up French company and took a sizeable number of good guys with him. Akash illustrated all too well that when a good professional leaves a company because of the feeling of being cheated or let down, he would be very vengeful and can do real damage to his ex-employer. Akash and his team not only took good guys from AMC but also took away many good customers and vendors along with them (Akash went on to make this French company a formidable competitor over a period of time). AMC suffered heavily because of Akash's departure but Baba was not bothered about such losses to the organization. His one and only focus was to strengthen his position at AMC. To reiterate this and to strengthen his philosophy of divide and rule further, he created a third position in the south called Regional General Manager, Chennai and awarded this position to another loyal wild dog.

TIGER AND THE WORKERS' UNION

Kelvin had started his career as a truck driver and went up to become a General Manager in the company. One must take cognizance of the fact that this is comparatively easy in a western firm than an Indian company. This journey also enabled Kelvin to acquire deep understanding of people at the bottom of the pyramid in an organization. This understanding helped him and Ben decide to take every Indian worker on Supernova-India's role rather than the usual practice of contract workers prevailing in India then. It was a very radical decision, but both Ben and Kelvin were fully prepared to take it forward as they were very clear that if a customer centric company has to be built, then it is very important to engage with every member of organization at every level. It was also a fact that the lower rung workers would physically spend more time with customers and thus were a very important link in the chain.

Looking back, Raman also realized that Kelvin could take this decision because Supernova management style was very hands on and there was no separate interface between employees and management especially in the form of HR/IR department. Kelvin would involve himself in every recruitment and training, and subsequent mentoring. Raman remembers one interesting incident. They were debating about uniform for workers and after discussing many ideas, Kelvin proposed jeans and T-shirt. His logic was very simple. He wanted his people to look smart and take pride in their work. Supernova must have been the first company in India way back in mid nineties to provide blue jeans and red T-shirts to its workers as uniform. Another initiative taken by Kelvin was to put the name of the driver on the truck he was driving. This brought out a great sense of ownership and pride and ensured that the drivers maintained their trucks well. Kelvin also had a habit of dropping in at sites especially during night shifts and would give a helping hand to workers. Supernova also made sure that the workers were provided with best health and safety gear and other facilities apart from a good salary.

Over the years, the workers of Supernova became the key differentiator between their company and their competitors in the eyes of their customers and this is what Kelvin had envisioned. During this journey, a few bad elements were also dealt with firmly. And so, in spite of very strong efforts by various labour unions, Supernova employees stayed away from joining a union. Normally, a union is formed only when the workers lose faith and trust in the managers they deal with, not necessarily the management. In majority of the cases, only when the house is not in order, does a worker seek an outside intervention.

Raman left Supernova in January 2002 and within six months, a workers' union was formed. When Raman heard this news while in Hyderabad, he had a lump in his throat. However, at that point, he had no clue that destiny would not allow him to be a silent spectator.

After the amalgamation of Supernova and AMC in 2006, Raman, had the mammoth task of taking Supernova and AMC as a combined entity (in Bangalore) along with the Supernova trade union. There was a fundamental difference between Supernova and AMC employment policies. At Supernova, everyone had a permanent company role whereas at AMC, there was a mix of company and contract employees. AMC also had a few contract trucks working for them and this was an absolutely non-negotiable issue with the Supernova union as they felt vulnerable with this arrangement. Initially, Raman was optimistic about his harmonious relationship with Supernova team, which had trusted him in the past, but very soon he realized that trade union roots were quite deep rooted and once established, very difficult to change. The workers refused to allow contract trucks at Supernova units. This was a difficult proposition to agree to because it would mean depriving the company of contract resources and deploying more capital to employ workers in a competitive atmosphere. Raman tried explaining to the Supernova workers that deployment of contract machinery would be need based and would not affect their current jobs but, the external union leaders continued to be adamant.

Across the world, managements often tend to underestimate the hold of unions on corporates and the same happened in this case too. Before both parties could come to any conclusion on this contentious issue, a parallel union was formed at the AMC works in Bangalore. The message was loud and clear. A lot of water had flown under the bridge after Raman's departure from Supernova and the stage was now set for a confrontation.

THE SHOWDOWN

The next few months were quite agonizing as the management and the union got locked into a boxing ring. One of the union members creating problems for the management was Swami. He was a driver with AMC and was actively involved with the union activity. On the other hand, there was a mole from the management side, loader operator Rao, who was known to Baba directly and would call him frequently (Raman realized later that Baba had such people all over for micro-management).

One day, it so happened that the AMC Bangalore operations head asked this loader operator to drive a truck as there was a shortage of drivers that day. When Rao started the truck, he got a call from Swami demanding that unless the management gave in writing that his designation was changed from loader operator to a truck driver, he would not operate the truck. Rao immediately called up Baba at Bombay and informed him about this incident. Baba, in turn, called up Swami and they both had a heated telephonic spat. Next day, all workers assembled in front of AMC Bangalore office with placards and posters, shouting slogans against Baba. Baba was the CEO of the company and the righteous tiger in Raman was totally upset with this act of insubordination. He decided to take concrete action because the production and efficiency was also getting badly affected by the day to day interference of the union. Raman had always believed that when confronted with a problem, it's better to take the bull by its horns, than avoiding the problem. After consulting Baba and the senior management team, he suspended Swami with immediate effect for pending charges against him. In the next three weeks, after completing the inquiry, the company sacked Swami from services. However with his dismissal, the entire Bangalore business with more than 300 direct employees and around 500 indirect employees came to a grinding halt. Also, in the meanwhile, anticipating this, AMC took an injunction order from court so as to continue operation under police protection.

Raman had no clue that he had invited a battle which would be fought only by him single-handedly as the wild dogs including Baba were more than happy to see him in this mess (in fact just two days after the strike began, Baba left for overseas to attend a technical training program). AMC Bangalore operations were strike-stricken for nearly three months and this is when Raman realized how archaic Indian labour laws were. It was clear to him that if one had to list the reasons why India would struggle to become a prosperous industrial nation, one major reason would be its ancient, outdated and one-sided labour laws. He also realized that, like management, the unions were rife with tiger and wild dog fights. Most workers are by and large work-orientated and would not like to escalate issues to a point of no return but they are vetoed by wild dogs amongst themselves.

Professionally and personally, this was one of the most painful periods in Raman's life as he was fighting against his own workforce which was so dear to him. During this period, he also came across Mr. Prasad and Mr. Reddy — Mr. Prasad being arguably one of the finest industrial relations lawyer in the country and Mr. Reddy, a hard core communist leader deeply married to the cause of workers' welfare.

Mr. Prasad was, at the time, one of the best brains in India on labour laws and what made him different from other legal consultants was that though he fought for the management, he was equally concerned about the fairness to the workers. He taught Raman the golden rule of being 'FAIR and FIRM' on labour issues.

Mr. Reddy was a hard core communist, who though a union leader, believed in fighting it out fair and square. Because of this sense of fairness that ran in him as well as Mr. Prasad, they had a mutual respect for each other. During the peak of the strike period, under advice from Mr. Prasad, Raman took a huge risk and shifted few trucks and machinery from Bangalore operations to their Pune and Chennai units, using outside drivers and with police protection. Though it resulted in violent protests from workers, it opened doors for the management to bring in those workers to work who wanted to leave the union. This led to breaking up of the union and eventually the strike was called off. The management was also able to pen down a long term agreement which completely safeguarded them against the risk of such an occurrence in the future.

Raman emerged a winner against all odds but was upset about having to deal with the workers with an iron glove, the very same workers who had built the organization with their blood and sweat. Through this experience, Raman also learnt that mergers and acquisitions rarely bring good results in the long run. Acquiring a company is easy but uniting the workforce from two different work cultures is next to impossible. Also, acquisitions are projected as an inorganic growth path designed by a few ambitious individuals, who, once the acquisition laurels are shared, cleverly dump it on someone else's shoulder to make the impossible happen. In this case, it was Baba and Chaila who took all the credit of acquiring Supernova and dumped it on Raman's head to do the impossible.

WILD DOGS CLOSING IN ON THE TIGER

During this period, Raman was also getting very upset and frustrated with the turn of events in the AMC organization structure and would often discuss his problems with his wife, who would calmly absorb it all. This would calm him too.

Despite numerous provocations by wild dogs and adverse situations, he remained focused on two fundamental guidelines taught by Kelvin for any adversity:

1. Remain focused on work. It is essentially your good work which will keep you afloat.

2. KMS or 'Keep your Mouth Shut' and let your work do the talking.

THE BEST CLIENTS AND
THEIR INFLUENCE

With his knowledge of the Bangalore market and with union issue a thing of the past, Raman was able to take business to a great high by the end of 2005. He was also able to spread the business beyond Bangalore. He could secure an order, against stiff competition (in fact Raman was offered a bribe by one of the main competitor which he politely declined), from one of the major software companies for their Mysore campus expansion, where AMC was asked to set up a ready mix concrete plant exclusively for this project. This software company was a very demanding customer and at the initial stage, Raman spent weeks together at the project site, putting things in place. After all the hard work, AMC reaped rich benefits from this project including a repeat order for this company's Hyderabad campus. And for a long time this software giant was AMC's single biggest customer.

Looking back, Raman considers this project as the most satisfying professional challenge of his life. He also had a very close interaction with this software company's top management and has a few observations to share about them.

1. This was one of the most transparent organizations one could ever deal with. Raman used to get purchase order worth millions just on an email and no one in the organization expected any payback for this. In fact, Raman

had not given a single gift to any one during his entire association with this customer. On the contrary, the customer's engineers used to take him out for a drink whenever he visited Mysore.

2. For more than five years, one of the senior directors would be at the Mysore site every Sunday, supervising every detail of construction.

3. Every drawing and even tiles would have the approval of the founder chairman, showing the level of commitment and involvement of the top management.

4. Any other organization or government might not have been able to create more than 500 acre plus world class campuses, as created by this company at Mysore. One appreciates this professionalism even more in the light of the recent Commonwealth games 2010 fiasco.

Raman's interaction with this company restored his faith in his own tigerly qualities, which by now were under serious threat from the wild dog pack. But for this company, where merit was evident everywhere, Raman might have changed his corporate beliefs. Looking back, it was providential to interact with this organization as it helped restore Raman's faith in his tigerly qualities.

BANGALORE TO MANGALORE

Mangalore had always attracted Raman for its business potential and despite the strong skepticism

(Baba was known to say, 'If we are successful it's us and if we fail it's YOU'), Raman started the Mangalore business in early 2006. Once again, he was going back to early ready mix concrete days of Bangalore as theirs was the first of its kind plant in Mangalore, and once more Raman had to sell the same concept, this time to the Mangalore market. However, this time Raman and his team were better prepared and the response from the Mangalore market was much better too. From the second month onwards, Mangalore remained a profitable business venture. Mangalore was also the first in the expansion of AMC's business in tier two cities.

By now, Baba, Chaila and the pack could see the tiger in Raman performing better in Bangalore market against all hurdles erected by them. Hence they decided to curtail Raman once and for all as they knew no one could question them, and so brought Mr. Opportunist back to Bangalore as the General Manager, Karnataka and very cleverly re-designated Raman as General Manager, rest of Karnataka (altogether a new business territory), which would include only Mysore and Mangalore. Raman was being suitably rewarded (sic) for starting and developing business at these locations and he became one of those rare professionals who were demoted thrice against proven and quantifiable performance. His career path was a downward spiral from GM-South India in 2002 to GM-Karnataka to GM-rest of Karnataka in 2007.

ROUND ONE GOES TO THE PACK

The above role change was very humiliating and Raman could see the end of road for himself at AMC since all along in his professional journey, he had believed that only performance mattered and the performer was always rewarded. After all, what matters most to any professional is a pat or a few encouraging words by his seniors at micro level and at the macro level, a good incentive or a rewarding promotion. Truly speaking, the wants of a good employee are very limited compared to his contributions.

By now, Raman was also convinced that performance is a very subjective thing in the corporate world and its assessment can vary from boss to boss. Raman also realized that the collective force of wild dogs could outsmart a tiger in any organization where the organizational core values were not aligned to the core values of the tiger. Hence, it is very important for every professional to work in an organization where he finds his individual values and beliefs in sync with the key people of organization. Only in such an organization would a professional blossom to his maximum potential.

Mr. Azim Premji of WIPRO is absolutely right when he says that 'People don't leave organizations, they leave managers'.

By the end of 2007, Raman had reached the end of his tether and opted to resign from AMC.

———•———

9

MUSCAT VIA THE BACKWATERS OF KERALA

Raman had always believed in God's ability to open a new window when a door was shut: within a month of his resignation from AMC, he got an unexpected call from an overseas placement agency for the position of General Manager with a reputed ready mix concrete company in Muscat, Oman. Raman was in two minds but as always it was his wife Meera who suggested de-stressing by taking a short break to the backwaters of Kerala.

These backwaters are one of those unique human

settlements in the world where people live below the sea level. The first few things which strike you are the lush green spread of paddy fields and lanes of water ways passing through small villages. These waterways are equivalent of the roads connecting various parts of the city and any form of connection between the outside world and the backwater settlement is through these water canals. Apart from the big tourist house boats, one will also find locals taking small boats for various daily activities of life. A typical house boat package includes check in at 12noon and check out the next day around 10am. The rooms are very nicely done up and an average-sized house boat would contain two to three well-appointed rooms. The front portion of the boat serves as the drawing and dining area. The boat is normally manned by three people. One is at the wheels, one mans the kitchen and the third man attends to the guests besides assisting the other two guys. The check in is followed by lunch which is freshly cooked on board as per instructions given by the guest in advance. The fare comprises of freshly caught sea food. The house boat eventually cruises to the main lake - the Vembanad Lake. The lake is spread over hundreds of sq km and the main body is around the Kumrakoam area of Kerala.

The boat travels at a leisurely speed of 5 to 10km per hour and the sight of paddy fields, coconut lagoons, various birds and gentle breeze makes you realize why these back water holidays are so popular with foreign tourists. In the entire journey, the sense of cleanliness and hygiene of this whole area is noteworthy.

During this short break in Kerala, Raman and Meera discussed various pros and cons of moving to Muscat. Oman, with its capital city Muscat, is one of the best places to work and live in the Middle East. The local population holds Indians in high esteem as Indians have contributed largely in building their nation after the discovery of oil. Muscat also has the distinction of building the first Hindu temple in the Middle East almost thirty years back. It also has Indian schools and a large Indian population. The salary and perks offered to Raman were good and the saving potential was brilliant as there was no tax on earnings. Raman would always remain indebted to Meera for making such complicated issues simple. She would always agree with Raman as long as he didn't make hasty decisions. In a typical corporate way, if Raman could put the facts properly across to her, she had an uncanny sense of clarity in arriving at the right conclusion. May be God has given this uncanny knack of intuitive decision-making to all women in that they know what is best for their family! By the time the Raos checked out of their house boat the next day, Raman was clear about Muscat.

Also Raman's belief in taking major decisions in life in a relaxed atmosphere proved successful once again.

———•———

10

THE MUSCAT EFFECT

The Seeb airport at Muscat is relatively small in size and when you are out on the main road, the lush landscaping on either side of the road is what strikes you foremost, considering the fact that the entire area is a desert. The rows of palm trees on either side of the road are very pleasing to the eye. As one continues the journey, one realizes that the traffic flows smoothly and no one ever honks. Raman was told by his Indian driver that honking is considered to be an insult to fellow drivers. Raman also noticed that lane discipline was followed as a rule. It is true that road sense reflects the discipline of any country and Raman mused that Indians would never observe traffic protocol quietly and spontaneously. In fact, a majority of foreigners have told Raman that they get paranoid when they get exposed to Indian roads.

Raman was taken to Ruwi, the down town area of Muscat and was put up at one of the best hotels in town. As his stay would be longer, he was provided with a suite where there was provision for cooking too. Raman's first few days were spent in completing all the necessary formalities required for an expatriate, like the medical checkup, getting resident visa and applying for the driving license. Raman realized how organized these formalities were at Muscat, compared to the agony an expatriate would experience in India.

Muscat as a city is very neat and beautiful with a clean beach. Raman decided to settle for one of the villas around the beach area and checked a few of them. He was really impressed with the overall quality. He also met the principal of the Indian school and was assured seats for his children. One thing which appealed to him the most about the school was that it believed in compulsory participation of all children in minimum two co-curricular activities. Raman also enrolled himself for driving lessons, which is mandatory before appearing for the driving test. After hearing stories about people not getting driving license even after several attempts, Raman was more than determined to crack it in the first attempt itself.

Raman had been offered the role of General Manager by Mr. Raghavan, the CEO of the group when they had met at the Taj, Bangalore. He was one of those rare Indians who had a good blend of eastern and western cultures. He hailed from an aristocratic Tamil Brahmin family and had studied in England. He had held senior positions with Voltas before moving to Muscat twenty years ago. At Muscat, he continued to hold senior positions and though was in his sixties, he looked dapper with a tall and lean built and a very intelligent, smiling face. Mrs. Raghavan, his elegant wife was a woman of substance and good taste.

After joining Zubair Plc, Muscat, Raman took no time in expressing his frustration about being away from his family, and Rags (as Raghavan was called) picked it up very quickly. Mr. and Mrs. Raghavan were very active in Muscat social echelons. So to help Raman overcome his homesickness, almost every evening he would be picked up by them and taken to various parties. Though Rags was very formal at office but on personal front his extra effort of helping Raman settle down in a new country is again a true attribute of a TIGER boss. These are precisely the fine qualities which segregate a leader from a manager.

Raman was also in touch with Sudeep and Shruti, relatives of his college days' friend, and it was Shruti who in her typical style asked Raman one day as to why he left his well-settled as well as well-paid job in India? Raman struggled to give a convincing answer.

Raman's next few days were really disturbed because the more he tried to find an answer to Shruti's innocent question, the more he realized that he had let the tiger in him down badly. He also realized that he was actually an escapist who had surrendered to the wild dogs and fled from the jungle. He had let down many people as after his resignation from AMC, almost fifty employees also quit AMC and Raman was sure that they had left primarily because of him and must be undergoing the same pain and trauma along with their family members as being faced by him.

In the next few days, Raman's shame graduated to severe anger. He felt pain for his loss of pride and the pride of so many colleagues like Naren, Akash, Satish, Giri, Jayesh, Sunil, Bindu and several others who were humiliated and marginalized by the master manipulator and his wild dogs. He realized that the tiger in him had compromised his biggest attribute — SELF-RESPECT and his entire future life would be futile if he had to live with this shame and guilt.

After days of introspection, Raman decided to fight back his lost pride.

After almost forty days of arrival in Muscat, he left for India on the pretext of recruitment. After reaching Bangalore, it took him two days to muster the courage to call up Rags and to break the news that he would not be coming back to Muscat. Rags was shell-shocked and took the next available flight to Bangalore. They met over breakfast and the gentleman in Rags handled the situation in a very dignified manner. Raman gave the excuse of not getting adjusted to Muscat life as the reason for his abrupt decision. Rags tried convincing but eventually they 'agreed to disagree'.

Raghavan is settled in Bangalore now and Raman and he share a friendly equation even today.

BEGINNING OF ROUND TWO

Raman was back in Bangalore by the end of December 2008 and once settled, gave a call to Chaila and expressed his desire to rejoin AMC. Master manipulator or Baba was more than happy to take Raman back as there were uncomfortable questions raised by the AMC board when Raman had left. Baba also made sure to announce to the world that Raman was back because of him. Also by now, the Indian economy was on roll and everyone was talking about growth. Baba was asked by the board to expand business rapidly and he needed someone to deliver growth for him. Since this was a very demanding role with several uncertainties and new market challenges, the chances of failure were high. With a clever master plan that failure at the job could be used against Raman to finish him while his success can be claimed by him, Baba offered the post of Head, Business Development to Raman. As by now he was mentally prepared for such games, Raman rejoined AMC with another new job profile, his fifth in six years.

The pack also ensured that Raman would have no say in purchase of machineries and contracts related to setting up units, though these were part of business development. These functions involving crores of rupees would remain reserved for select members of the pack only.

This approach reinforced Raman's belief that the very genesis of wild dog packs in any walk of life is GREED and that is the common link between all scams, be it the Commonwealth games, Adarsh or Defence Deals.

———————•———————

11

THE NEW AGE TIGER

Raman in his new avatar realized that he must re-align his tigerly attributes to fight the pack effectively. The first action was to improve his sensory and his listening capabilities. Raman also encouraged some of the wild dogs who were sitting on the fence to change their loyalty. It's a fact that every professional has innate tigerly qualities in him and it's only the situation or manipulative bosses which forces him to join the pack.

He also learnt to fully comprehend finer details before jumping to conclusions (both his early days' mentors SKS and Kelvin were impulsive and in turn made him impulsive too). He also decided to work on another tigerly quality – Patience. Raman realized quite late in his career that, at times it is better to show patience and resilience, when encountered with a good or bad situation. By giving adequate time:

(a) The picture gets clearer, so as to make a better decision.

(b) Time itself throws up a solution.

However one must not lose sight of the problem, otherwise patience turns into procrastination and these two aspects have a thin dividing line between them. Procrastination is also a tool used by the likes of Baba to kill a performer slowly and gradually.

TALK THERAPY FOR NEW AGE TIGER

While in Muscat, Raman came across a best-selling book of the sixties on Transactional analysis 'GAMES PEOPLE PLAY' by the psychologist Eric Berne where he talked about elaborate and restricted talk. Raman was quick to realize that the tiger in him also needed to move from restricted talking style to elaborate talking style. A tiger in a forest can afford to roar as and when he wishes but a tiger in a corporate set up needs to be more articulate and savvy and must roar only in exceptional situations.

Raman made it a habit to practice the art of elaborate talk.

Raman also realized that a tiger hunts alone and does not encourage coterie. Human beings, by and large, need ego massages and the bigger the profile of a person, the greater is the possibility of him being surrounded by a coterie. A coterie can not only misguide you, it can also disconnect you from reality. One cannot eliminate it completely but can minimize and balance it with good influences around. History would testify that majority of power centers collapsed because of coterie.

Hence, Raman decided to have a good core team (not a coterie) around him. After all, you are as good as your team.

TIGER AND HIS TEAM

Harith had joined as a trainee engineer way back during Raman's Supernova's days and had turned out to be a good operations guy with his brilliant industrial engineering background. He had also handled the Mysore software company's project very successfully and was appreciated by the client. Raman and he had shared a good comradeship then and had enjoyed working with each other, without compromising their professional ethics and integrity, and staying equally committed to organizational goal. Raman still recollects one incident when they were off to Mysore on work and Harith was driving Raman's vehicle. The vehicle in front of them stopped suddenly and Harith, because of slow reaction, could not avoid colliding with the vehicle ahead, which was being driven by an old man. In the normal course, they would have put the blame on the other guy, but in this case they accepted their mistake. They also had a choice of going to the police station and taking the insurance route but this would have delayed their meeting with the client. Hence they decided to get the estimate done on the other car at Mandya, the nearest town, and it came to around thirty thousand rupees. Raman paid the money. After a few days, Harith came to him with a cheque of the same amount as he felt the accident was totally his own fault. After a prolonged debate, they agreed to share the cost. However, the important fact here is that, they could have easily claimed it from the company, as Raman was a cheque signatory up to hundred million rupees and Harith, his immediate subordinate, was authorized to clear purchases up to ten million rupees. But not even once did the thought come to their mind that they could manipulate the whole thing to their advantage. There may not be a better example of practicing propriety and staying true to one's conscience in the corporate world.

Vijayan was a brilliant cost accountant, again from Supernova. He had pleasing manners and good interpersonal skills and had the ability to wear several hats unlike many straight-jacketed finance guys. Vijayan's strength was in getting all statutory approvals required for starting Greenfield operations with minimum speed money, the common terminology in corporate world for graft. He would ensure that his paperwork for approvals from the government department, be it inspector of factories or pollution control, would be absolutely perfect in the long run (Vijayan never took shortcuts).

Vinay had done brilliantly well in Masters (in Engineering) and was recruited by Raman himself into Supernova. While in Supernova, one morning the security informed Raman that there was a young guy who wanted to see him. As he was busy, he spoke to this person over the intercom. Vinay introduced himself as a young civil engineer, with a master's degree, looking for a job. Instead of saying a curt no, for some strange reason, Raman said he was busy and that Vinay could wait if he wanted to. After a while, Raman forgot about it and at around 7pm, while going back home, the security informed him that Vinay was still waiting for him and that he hadn't moved an inch from the security cabin the entire day. Raman felt really bad for him and apologized, to which he replied, "Sir, it is ok. I really want to work with you." Over the years, Vinay shaped out to be a brilliant technical hand.

Very soon Raman made a core team of these three guys, one with operational and other two with finance and technical backgrounds, a must-have combination for starting any business development venture successfully (right from selection of land, recruitment of people and the first sale until the business stabilized) at more than a dozen locations across India. They worked hard and partied harder. Taking a clue from Raman, these three also visited almost all the temples across the country for the Almighty's blessings.

Raman's team turned out to be his biggest strength against the wild dogs pack. However on their part, the pack in general and Baba in particular, left no stone unturned to corner and frustrate these three guys.

THE WILD DOGS' PACK CONTINUES TO BITE

One of the unique characteristic of packs in every organization is their ability to strike when least expected. And mostly the sufferer would be one of the most righteous and performing man in the organization.

Raman was able to negotiate and buy a very good piece of industrial land at a throw away price at Lucknow from a leading builder, purely on the basis of personal relations he forged with Mr. Gupta, the Chairman of the this building group. Based on this success, AMC decided to start their first business venture in the Hindi heartland way back in 2008 end. The biggest challenge Raman had at that point of time was to find the right man to take business forward and very quickly it was clear to Raman that getting a person with right specification and with the rider that he should be local was getting nowhere. It was during this phase, Raman was told about Ramprakash, a young civil engineer working with a leading cement company, who could be the candidate Raman was looking for.

Raman saw in Ramprakash a young version of himself, confident, hands on, intelligent and above all, with an aura of integrity. Ramprakash and Raman developed a mutual respect for each other and Ramprakash was more than keen to work under an industry leader. Together they formed a formidable team and with support from Harith, Vijayan and Vinay (Raman's core team), Lucknow started making profit in less than six months of operation and continued to for a long time.

As success always comes in a package, the problem in Lucknow plant came from a very strange corner. Baba had employed a watchman, in his residential building at Mumbai, whose nephew was barely tenth pass and was looking for a job. Incidentally this watchman was from U.P and when he came to know about AMC's Lucknow operation, he pleaded to Baba for accommodating his nephew at Lucknow. As Baba believed in having his own people at strategic places, he prevailed upon Ramprakash to accommodate this boy Anand Mishra as a helper at the Lucknow unit.

Things were normal for the next few months and then one day there was an argument between Anand Mishra and the factory security guard for some trivial reason. Within an hour, Ramprakash got a call from Baba asking him to remove the security guard. When Ramprakash checked with Raman on how to go about it, Raman asked him to be fair and conduct an inquiry into the whole incident before taking any decision. After the enquiry, few things emerged:

1. Anand Mishra had been in regular touch with Baba.

2. He also had a habit of taking loans from fellow workers and would repay them as he deemed fit, by flaunting his proximity to Baba.

3. He was so sure of his high powered proximity that during the course of enquiry, he threatened even Ramprakash of dire consequences, if he tried to meddle around with him.

Raman decided to act on this and during his next visit to Lucknow gave a good dressing down to Anand Mishra in front of everyone and also advised Ramprakash to be focused on his work and not to pay much attention to petty politics. Raman thought that this would be the end of the entire episode without having slightest of the idea the danger looming ahead.

Almost six months after this incident, when Raman

was no more responsible for Lucknow operations, he got a call from Ramprakash who was in tears. The only thing he could say was, "Sir, I am leaving."

In every manufacturing industry, stock/inventory is always a grey area and normally the practice is to see whether the stock, which fluctuates from month to month, evens out at regular intervals. It seems Baba and his team was keeping a watch on Lucknow stocks and was maintaining a stoic silence as long as things were under control. One month, for no fault of Ramprakash, when the stock showed a negative variance, Baba along with few others descended on Lucknow (Baba had otherwise made very few business visits to Lucknow in the past) and went to the extent of accusing Ramprakash of selling cement outside. Ramprakash was shocked and couldn't believe this was coming from the top management of the company he had helped build from scratch in the last two years. He resigned immediately. This incident reinforced Raman's belief in wild dog philosophy of protecting their people at any level and at any cost.

GOLD AND GLITTER

During his business developmental role at AMC, which required several days of travelling across the length and breadth of the country, Raman had many interesting people interactions. One such day of travel was truly memorable.

On 25th May, 2009 when he was travelling between Bangalore and Raipur, he took an early morning flight to Mumbai before taking a connecting flight to Raipur. He usually preferred an emergency door aisle seat as it would offer more leg room and the middle seat would invariably be empty. To his surprise, that day he had a young pretty girl sitting next to him who was snoozing before he sat. When breakfast was served, they started talking. She was working as an air hostess with the same airline and was en route to Pune. During their conversation, Raman realized how difficult and strenuous the job of an airhostess could be. For a flight that departed at 6am, they would have to report at the airport by 4.30am. Since they would be put up on a twin sharing basis in the hotel, and dressing up would take considerable time, they would have to be up by 2.30am. Also they would do a minimum 3 to 4 sectors, at times even more, which meant 8 to 10 hours on their feet at high altitudes and in pressurized cabins. Add to this the tantrum thrown by some passengers who believe that by buying an airline ticket, they can boss the cabin crew around!

After hearing this young lady's story, Raman's perception of so called glamorous and high flying airhostesses changed for the better since he realized that all that glittered was not gold.

He landed in Mumbai at around 7.30am and headed to the premium lounge on the first floor after going through security as his Raipur flight was a bit later. The lounge was almost empty but for Aamir Khan and Javed Akhtar (Both known names of the film industry) deeply engrossed in a conversation at a corner table. He deliberately seated himself next to these two gentlemen and waited for an appropriate opportunity to interact with them. By and large, he had seen celebrities and public figures trying to put up a larger than life image and throwing their weight around at airports and public places, hence, he was curious to see the real side of these two intellectuals of the Indian film industry. After a few minutes, Javed Akhtar left and Raman took the opportunity to say hello to Aamir Khan. The first thing that struck him about Aamir was his honesty. Aamir responded very warmly and accepted his compliments gracefully. He also took interest in Raman's work and was genuinely nice to him. So in the early morning hours of that day, Raman had encountered an airhostess with a supposedly glittering profession and then met the king of celluloid glitter. Beneath the veneer, they were simply human beings.

TWENTY-FOUR CARAT GOLD

Later in the morning his flight to Raipur landed at around 10.30am. By the time he was out of the airport building, he could feel the hot blistering sun at 40 degrees plus. His car, with the driver holding the placard, was ready for Raman. After Raman got into the car and started moving, he noticed an armed force officer walking down the road. Raman asked the driver to slow down and offered a lift to the officer. He turned out to be Major Balwant Singh from the artillery, who had also been on the same flight as Raman. He had been to Rajasthan border to attend a course on T56 Tanks. This Major was candid enough to tell Raman that he couldn't afford to hire a cab to go to the railway station and hence decided to walk to the nearest bus stop, a minimum of three kilometres. He also said that compared to the temperature inside a military tank in Rajasthan, the 40 degrees plus temperature at Raipur that morning was nothing. This officer was from a village in Haryana and had a two year old son, whom he had last seen sixteen months back. He also mentioned to Raman that only two days back his son was asking for a pack of chips which was supposed to be a special treat. After hearing this, Raman could not help himself from asking the Major, what kept him going in that army job against all this hardship. After a brief few moments, the army Major said that there could be three reasons.

One, every family in his village had at least one member in the army. Two, almost every male in his family was in the army. Thirdly and most importantly, he said that his job would provide him an honourable death. He summed it by saying that our nation would celebrate his death with a twenty one gun salute. This revelation hit Raman hard as all the comforts of a corporate job could not guarantee a dignity and honour in death. On the contrary, one could never gauge who would bother to even turn up at the funeral and shed genuine tears for the departed.

Raman instantly realized that his third encounter of the day was with twenty four carat gold with real glitter and a real tiger too.

———•———

12

THE SILVER LINING

In early 2009, a survey was done by a leading business magazine in collaboration with a business school in Bangalore to identify Business Innovators, people who brought about change in their chosen profession. For his contribution in changing the form and usage of concrete in Bangalore, Raman was chosen amongst the three luminaries and was felicitated at a glittering function. He was also featured on the magazine's cover page. When lady luck shines, it shines bright. Raman was also elected as the President of a leading professional body and was inducted in the governing council of a leading business school. He became a regular invitee speaker at important forums. During this period, he also presented several technical papers at national and international seminars. The tiger in him started to command due attention now.

All of the above raised Raman's profile. One day in a conference, he met with the Managing Director of one of his firm's major competitors. In the days that followed, Raman was offered the position of the Chief Executive Officer. Raman politely declined the offer as CEO and also informed about it to the AMC top management. A few months later, out of the blue came the position of head of AMC's all India business and Raman was the obvious choice. This was a dream come true for him. By then, AMC had almost fifty units in thirty cities across the country. A majority of these units had been established by Raman and his team during his development stages.

Raman felt that his return from Muscat was after all a good decision. Another major development during this period was that Mr. Ramakrishnan or RK, AMC chairman's trusted man, was made Managing Director of AMC. Baba was made to report to him. Mr. RK was a fortyish, brilliant, IIT-IIM graduate and was, for Raman, one of the brightest bosses to work with. Raman had a comfortable equation with him and was backed by him whole-heartedly whenever required. Raman also learnt a lot from him, especially the number crunching skills.

RAISING THE BAR

Soon after taking charge as Head of AMC's all India business, Raman presented three growth plans to the board — a short term (for a period of one to three months), medium term (three to six months duration) and long term (six months to three years). He also presented a well-thought out 'vision plan' for the organization.

ORGANIZATIONAL STRUCTURE

The topmost priority in his short term plan was to have an organizational structure. Till then, everything started and ended with Baba and Chaila. Though there was a well-qualified HR head, he had been reduced to a mere catering manager and was made to join the wild dog pack as Mr. Fixer.

Under this new short term plan, the company's business was divided into eight regions with regional heads heading it. Within each region were business managers for different locations reporting to the regional head. With logistics being the key to this business, the region size was restricted to 300 to 500 sq km. The functional managers i.e. sales, technical, operation and finance, reported to the business managers. This structuring had the following plusses —

1. It was all done with in-house talent and no new recruitment was needed.

2. It was done against the wishes of the pack and obviously they tried every trick under their belt (including hacking Raman's mails) either to sabotage it or to put their people in strategic positions.

3. The company did not lose a single talent even after this restructuring.

It was Raman's ability to demonstrate fair leadership that made this restructuring possible. After all, most employees in any organization can see the difference between a manipulator and a leader and they respond accordingly.

FOCUSING ON CRITICAL BUSINESS LOCATIONS

Raman's medium term plan was to turn around cash losing locations to, at least, cash profit situation and in its first phase, Delhi and Calcutta topped this list. Delhi was a disintegrated unit and Calcutta had an ineffective leader who was an opportunist wild dog.

With Delhi, Raman had an advantage. His command of Hindi made him a good communicator and he used it to the fullest to build bridges with the team there. The Delhi team was divided into two groups and to Raman's surprise one of the groups was headed by a senior manager, who was more into network selling of consumables than the company products! Raman made clear to this person that he was willing to give him a chance provided he focused on his work and played by the rules. Raman knew from experience that the only way to make such people tow the line was to be very firm with them. He addressed the team collectively on a few occasions and touched their conscience by asking them to give back to company which had been good to them for so many years in spite of the region accruing losses. Good sense prevailed quickly and with a clear direction, things started moving. Raman also mobilized a few good operational guys from other parts of business who demonstrated on-the-ground best practices, and also initiated morning 8 o'clock meetings. Finally a system was put in place to monitor all activities.

The Calcutta head, much against the wishes of the core pack leaders, was asked to leave by Raman and his second in command, Dutta, though not very experienced, was made the new head. Raman was also shocked to see that the local team had till then kept one unit, out of the three units at Calcutta, deliberately non-operational on flimsy grounds. He also discovered quickly that there were many fundamental problems in Calcutta such as the sales guys who had no two wheelers to move around and were commuting for sales calls on public transport. One main reason for this was that many were recruited at a low salary, and going by Kelvin's principle, if you pay peanuts, you get monkeys.

Raman took two gambles in Calcutta. One was to ask a relatively less experienced guy to head the business and another was to start the Salt Lake unit which had been shut for months. Raman took a chance on this relatively less experienced guy based on Kelvin's teaching that if the house is in order and if the leader is willing to give his best, any organization would succeed. However this approach also meant spending considerable time in Calcutta which also included visiting the Kali temple and Dakshineshwari for divine intervention regularly. His father's teaching of relying on spirituality helped him forge ahead with confidence and stay grounded despite heady success. The new business head, Dutta, also responded wholeheartedly and learnt the ropes from Raman quickly. This experiment reinforced Raman's belief in empowering and getting results from younger generation.

Both Delhi and Calcutta became cash positive in the third and fourth month itself.

THE UNTAPPED POTENTIAL

Raman's second mid-term priority was to scale up operations in Mumbai. A simple calculation established that with 20% increase in AMC's Bombay volume, the company would add 5% to the bottom line (Bombay having the highest realization in the country, thanks to the soaring sq. ft. prices). Over the years, the pack, under Baba's and Chaila's patronage, had ensured that Bombay business was never discussed in detail because it would have led to many skeletons tumbling out of the closet. Raman was also very clear about his objectives in Mumbai and did not engage in fault finding mission or petty politics. But as things started unfolding, there was one incident which proved once again that for Baba and the pack, personal interest was always placed above organizational interest.

AMC had one unit at Kurla, Mumbai and the land lease was coming to an end in a few months' time. The pack, including Baba, painted the picture that the owner of the land was asking a fancy price for lease renewal and the company should start looking for a new location. The management, including RK and Raman took it at face value. However, in one of the review meeting of Mumbai business, a very junior finance guy pointed out to Raman that even if the company had to rent Kurla land paying one and a half times, the company would be making good money. When Raman confronted Chaila with this data, he fumbled and gave him the details of the owner to negotiate directly. To Raman's surprise, the owner settled for a 20% increase and AMC continued to do business from the Kurla unit. Raman came to know later that with his success in Delhi and Calcutta, this was a well-planned sabotage move by Baba and the wild dog pack. Closure of the Kurla unit would have hit the bottom line of the entire company badly and would have put Raman in bad light. Also if they had moved away from Kurla land, the competitors would have moved in there. So with one stroke, the pack would have knocked down Raman twice. In just four months, the Mumbai region started doing all time high volumes and the bottom line of company swelled up healthily.

PUTTING FUNDAMENTALS IN PLACE

Raman's third and last mid-term objective was to improve productivity and collections and since these two parameters were also close to MD RK's philosophy, he gave Raman a free hand to drive it.

PAYMENT COLLECTION

Kelvin had drilled into Raman's head that no sale is complete without the money getting into the kitty. However at AMC, these parameters were never practised in a business manner in the past. Hence, to bring focus to collections, Raman came out with the following innovative solutions.

1. The sales team was told that any bad debt would affect their yearly increment and promotions so it was advisable to be extremely careful while extending credit (it is better to filter a customer at the beginning than chasing him later for payment).They were also advised to discuss credit terms firmly in the initial discussions itself

because most of the times, the sales people soft-paddle this touchy issue fearing they might antagonize the customer. Raman firmly believed that one should be upfront about this with the customer. His standard line used to be, "We would not compromise on quality and service, however payment terms once frozen are not negotiable."

2. No credit was given unless due diligence of the customer was done and the credit approval form was dully filled. The form would have details like customer banker's detail, referrals etc. This exercise would also expose the real intention of the customer, that is whether he was interested in having credit or had the intention to cheat, as those with latter would refuse to part with such information! Raman firmly believed that it was better to lose a customer, who had dubious intention, than to have him in the fold, because the time spent on collecting a bad debt is many times more than acquiring a new customer. The sales team was also asked to push maximum advance payment and to give credit only against instruments such as bank guarantee, letter of credit or as a last resort a post dated cheque.

3. Raman had learnt with experience that though extending credit to a customer is essential in any business the issues related to credit are often done in a very casual or informal manner. So,

to bring focus to credit control, Raman instructed his team to have a separate dossier for all customers who were extended credit and, it must contain all document like delivery docket, bills, reminder to customer (Raman insisted his team take acknowledgement of this as at times the customer would pretend they never received any communication!), reconciliation statements on regular basis or any other relevant document related to customer. Raman also instructed his team to carry this dossier as and when they visited the customer for a follow up because a document during discussion always brings seriousness to an issue.

4. Raman had also learnt over the years that Indians, by and large, would not like to default but would like to procrastinate on payment as long as it was possible. The challenge therefore, he would say to his team, is to, "Upgrade our payment in his list of priorities!" Raman was also very clear that one must not burn bridges with the customer over payment issue. Hence the only mantra to recover payment is to do constant follow up with the decision maker (not the gate keepers at lower level) without losing cool.

5. Raman also formed a core team of credit controllers whose job was to monitor collection very closely.

6. Most importantly was Raman's personal

involvement (Raman would spend a considerable time visiting customers).

Raman always believed that a good business leader must be involved in three core activities without fail:

(a) HSE i.e. Health, Safety and Environment issues.

(b) Quality and Innovation.

(c) Credit Control.

(Raman would diligently attend all safety and credit control meetings every month without fail.)

The above efforts brought very good results and the collection percentage against sale on monthly basis started showing a figure in excess of 100%, which meant that whatever was sold, the money was collected in the very same month.

SWEATING OF ASSET

During the year 2005-08, when the global and Indian economy were doing extremely well, AMC board decided to go on an aggressive expansion mode and in this process AMC had set up their business in more than fifty cities in the country. However, though the top line showed marginal increase, the bottom line remained under pressure. Raman had always believed in SKS philosophy that one must look at company asset as if one has spent his own money to acquire it.

In other words, the asset must be put to best use. In case of AMC, the main challenge was about the number of trips the trucks made in a day. Raman gave instruction to his operations team that if a truck is not transporting minimum 600 cubic meter of readymix concrete per month, then the operations team would be taken to task. One simple measure like this showed multifold results — the sales team started targeting jobs in the vicinity of plants, the pumps started pumping more volumes and in turn, the concrete plant started producing more volume on monthly basis and also, the number of hired trucks reduced — bringing direct saving to company. As a result, a healthy Return on Investment {ROI} started showing. However, all this was made possible by continuous monitoring by Raman and his core team, as there were many road blocks and resistance from several quarters.

———•———

13

THE TIGER ROARS

In ten months flat, since Raman took over as Head-All India Business, the top line, bottom line and collections hit an all-time high in the entire 14 year history of AMC. This was also the period in Raman's life when he extensively traveled and covered length and breadth of the country (In 3 months' time, he was airborne 79 times).

The result of his team's hard work was evident, loud and clear for everyone to behold. He also realized during this period that there were many extraordinary individuals in AMC who had immense potential which could be tapped with gentle guidance and in a facilitative atmosphere. When given a chance, these people really could do wonders. This fact further reinforced his belief that all extraordinary feats are always done by ordinary people with the right direction and guidance.

He wished that Kelvin and Mike were there to see this success because after all these years, the TIGER was performing with his pride intact. In March 2010, after a marathon budget meeting of three days in Delhi, Raman along with his regional heads and other key members flew to Jammu and from there traveled to Vaishnao Devi to pay tributes to the Goddess. Raman certainly had special thanks to offer.

By now, the rules of the game had changed and new yardsticks were put in place to measure performance. AMC was no more a bastion of wild dog packs and their manipulative skills. An umpire in RK was also put in place who would take stock of things periodically.

The AMC board was delighted and there was a clear road map for the next five years. Also Raman was very clear that he must have a successor in place in three years' time as in his view:

1. Change in leadership within a time frame is

necessary in every organization because business dynamics are always changing.

2. Power in the long run corrupts.

THE BUSINESS MANTRA

Raman's advice for any business head to be successful would be as follows:

1. Correct benchmarking of current reality, preferably in numbers.

2. Proper assessment of market potential and reach of the market.

3. Critical analysis of team and timely correction.

4. Cohesion among the team members of various departments — (One of Raman's favourite example in all meetings used to be the flying pattern of birds in a 'V' formation which eases the flying effort).

5. Competitor analysis in a systematic manner.

6. Activity specific road map.

7. Interaction with as many customers as possible.

8. Handling company money and assets as your own money and property, with utmost prudence.

9. Rewarding the team in a timely manner. Kelvin had taught him that any reward should be given when it is due as it loses its charm after a point.

10. Last but not the least, a boss has to earn respect i.e. he should be competent, and fair. He should be above all biases i.e. caste, creed, language, colour etc and absolutely honest. These qualities are vital and non-negotiable.

—•—

14

FINAL STOP OF THE SAFARI RIDE

Raman remembered his father telling him that Indian philosophy always believed in the power of good over bad. Throughout his professional journey, there were many times when this belief of Raman was put to test and was shaken. At such times, he wanted to give up and run away. But today, after twenty five eventful years of his corporate journey, the message Raman has for all the professionals in the corporate jungle, who are facing the wild dog packs and the likes of Baba, Chaila and others, is to 'Hold on to your tigerly traits'. For this, one must work on his tigerly qualities like team building, mastering the art of elaborate talk and being a thinker finisher. After all, life is not about short gains but is a sustained journey where, people should be proud of their professional milestones and experiences when they look back. In the long run, no matter how hard the fight is, truth always triumphs.

SATYAMEVA JAYETE

—•—

ACKNOWLEDGMENTS

The idea of writing a book had always been there at the back of my mind. Today when I have done so, I am finding it difficult to pen down this section because I need to acknowledge the efforts of so many people who have made this possible.

To keep it simple, I would thank them all in the same order in which they contributed as my story progressed.

A meeting with Pavan Choudary (a renowned author himself) after almost thirty years (we were together in the boarding school) was the point of inspiration. He encouraged me to put my thoughts to paper. Thanks Pavan for restoring my faith in myself and making me believe that I can do it.

Pavan also introduced me to Anu Anand, my publisher, who heard my narration patiently over the phone. She has this amazing listening quality and a knack of doing things collectively, taking into consideration everyone's interests. If I write again, I would like that book to be published by none but her.

When I started writing, I kept getting the feeling that I am wasting my time and that this would be a misadventure. This is where my elder daughter Tanvi and my dear wife Valsala came to my rescue. Tanvi encouraged me with constructive criticism and Valsala as always endorsed my endeavour with a smile. How can I forget Rhea, my younger daughter, who was there to attend to my simple needs like offering me a glass of water!

Once I was half way through, I was obsessed with writing. I would write late into the night or early in the morning and our pug Zoozoo would always be next to me or rather between my feet. His unconditional support was heart warming. He is no more and I miss you Zoozoo.

Rahul, my nephew, is the only male member in the family who shares a one-to-one relation with me, though we have an age gap of almost three decades.

Rahul scanned my first draft with all its deficiencies and offered valuable comments. Thanks Rahul for having the patience to go through it.

I thank Anamika Viswanathan, my official editor, who painstakingly worked for over six months or rather combed every word and sentence and made it into a presentable document. I have no doubt in mind that without her professional skill, this book wouldn't have seen the light of the day. I would also like to thank Mrs. Rashmi Bhattathiri who did the final proof reading and made the book more reader friendly.

I also thank my well-wishers and friends who believed in my story-telling abilities and encouraged me to embark on this journey.

At a professional level, I am thankful to many brilliant professionals who have left an indelible mark in my professional life. This book would not have been possible without their insights.

Mr. P.N.C Menon, Chairman — Sobha Developers, my current mentor/employer and a man with a human touch, who taught me the importance of numbers in professional life.

Mr. A Ramakrishna, (ex DMD — L&T) doyen of the Indian construction industry, my first mentor, who encouraged and supported my learning aptitude at an early stage of career.

Mr. A.K Chatterjee, ex Executive Director — ACC, a visionary, who pioneered and gave Ready Mixed Concrete Industry a corporate status way back in the early nineties.

Mr. B.R Rao, my boss in my early days at L&T, who demonstrated that one can work with conviction and belief.

Mr. Ken Cowie, ex MD Fletcher challenge — Ken helped me to transform as a global manager under Indian conditions.

Late Mr. Kevin McGowan — 'I owe you everything, Kevin'. You taught me how to remain 100% ethical even in difficult times.

Mr. John Wilkinson, ex CEO — RMC Readymix who encouraged me to do formal learning from the UK as a mature student of 40.

Mr. Mike Kar and Mr. James Brooks, two of the finest expatriate professionals in the Indian ready mix concrete business whom I have ever worked with.

Mr. K.C Ramamurthy, IPS (retired) and M/s Infosys, the two most wonderful customers I am proud to have dealt with.

Mr. B.C Prabhakar, my guru on industrial relations.

Mr. Vijay Agarwal, MD — Johnson Tiles who

taught me how to harness controlled aggression and remain totally focused.

Mr. Ganesh Kaskar, my boss for more than a decade who taught me, amongst many things, how to be a good listener.

Mr. Venugopal Panicker, perhaps the only professional CA I know who can do multi-skilling efficiently.

Mr. Koushika, who in my view is the best concrete professional in the country today.

K.P Murli, Sunil Kumar, Raghunath, V.J Murlidharan, Vinod, Koushik Datta, Prakash Menon, Jagannath, Ravi Kumar, Satish, Sunil George, Shriprakash Aggarwal, Ashok Mundra, Dinesh, Shaju, Prakash Pujar, Girinath, Denish, Urvija, and many more who were my peers and partners in the many battles which we fought together.

And, Chandrika, my secretary of many years, who made my day at work so organized.

Finally, a big thank to the Almighty who gave me courage to believe in myself.

———•———

ABOUT THE AUTHOR

Raj Pillai, 48, is presently Executive Director at the Concrete Products Division of Sobha Developers Ltd, a Bangalore-based leading real estate company.

A graduate in Civil Engineering from Bangalore University, Raj has over 25 years of industry experience. He also has a managerial course in Concrete and Quarrying applications, UK under his belt.

Raj has been associated with commercial Ready Mixed Concrete business for the last 17 years. He was instrumental in setting up and operating one of the first commercial Ready Mixed Concrete plants in India way back in 1995. Raj has also been responsible for taking the concept of Ready Mixed concrete to Tier 2 and 3 cities across the length and breadth of the country.

Raj Pillai was also Chairman of 'Indian Concrete Institute — Bangalore Centre' from 2008-11 and was responsible for various innovative path-breaking activities like conceptualizing DEMINAR 2009 and 2010 (International Seminar cum Live technical Demonstration). All these activities are testimonies to Raj's continuous endeavour to improve the quality of concrete in India. Currently Raj is the elected Vice President (South) of Indian Concrete Institute. Raj is also on his second term of 'Executive Council Member of Karnataka Employers Association', a body comprising more than 650 companies, engaged in improving industrial relationships at the work place. He is also an active member of the Institute of Concrete Technology, UK and Institute of Quarrying, UK.

For his outstanding work in promoting quality commercial Ready Mixed concrete in India, Raj was awarded the 'CHANGE MASTER' award by Tasmac University and Business Gyan Magazine way back in 2006. Recently, Raj has been conferred with the 'VISHWAKARMA AWARD 2012' by CIDC – a body of Planning Commission of the Government of India, for his contribution to the Indian construction industry.

Raj lives in Bangalore with his wife Valsala and daughters Tanvi and Rhea.

———•———